Dave Ramsey's

MILITARY EDITION

"Having worked with our men and women in uniform for several years, I've seen first-hand how personal financial troubles can distress—and even devastate—our servicemembers. That's why I'm such a huge fan of Dave Ramsey's *Financial Peace Military Edition*. It's the most complete, well-designed and easy-to-implement financial training available, and I'd love to see every military family experience the joy and peace that comes from taking control of their money for good!"

—Zig Ziglar

"Debt distracts from the mission. Debt erodes determination and obliterates vision. Debt is a devious and dangerous foe. It can be defeated but only with the right resources, the perfect plan and flawless execution. In order to serve our country effectively, you need to have the right equipment. Part of that gear is Dave Ramsey's *Financial Peace Military Edition*. I pray for your safety always, but I will worry a little less about you and your family if you ally with Dave Ramsey to defeat debt."

—Rabbi Daniel Lapin

Published by THE LAMPO GROUP, INC. For more information, please contact DAVE RAMSEY's office at 888.22.PEACE.

TABLE OF CONTENTS

Letter from Dave...5

Super Saving
Common Sense for Your Dollars and Cents.................................7

Relating with Money
Nerds and Free Spirits Unite!.. 21

Cash Flow Planning
The Nuts and Bolts of Budgeting.......................................29

Dumping Debt
Breaking the Chains of Debt..53

Credit Sharks In Suits
Understanding Credit Bureaus and Collection Practices.............67

Buyer Beware
The Power of Marketing on Your Buying Decisions.....................89

Clause and Effect
The Role of Insurance in Your Financial Plan.......................95

From Fruition To Tuition
Planning for Retirement and College..................................105

Real Estate and Mortgages
Keeping the American Dream from Becoming a Nightmare.............119

That's Not Good Enough!
How to Buy Only Big, Big Bargains...................................133

Working In Your Strengths
Careers and Extra Jobs...141

Of Mice and Mutual Funds
Understanding Investments..151

Financial Forms..161

From the Founder of FPM

I will never forget my visit to Normandy, where on June 6, 1944, the United States and its allies conducted the most massive military undertaking in recorded history. I stood at the top of the cliff overlooking Omaha Beach. Behind me was a cemetery where almost 9,400 of our servicemembers were buried. Far below me was the scene of that day's bloodiest battle.

Before dawn, members of the 82nd and 101st Airborne jumped from low-flying planes into the darkness, having no clue if they would live to hit the ground, or what they would face when they got there.

As dawn broke, 160,000 men hit the beaches along a 25-mile stretch. Once they made it to the sand, they faced impenetrable cliffs that rose straight up, topped by enemy troops with machine guns just waiting for the kill.

It was a day filled with incredible acts of personal courage, and by sunset, a foothold was secured and the end of the Nazi reign of terror had begun.

As I looked down on that beach that day, I thought, *If there's anything our organization can do to bless the men and women who are willing to make that kind of sacrifice, we want to do it.*

To that end, I am excited to welcome you to this special military edition of *Financial Peace University*. This is a class that has changed the lives of hundreds of thousands of families, and now we're pleased to present it to you, our honored men and women in uniform.

As you work through the training, be sure to watch for the special military-specific information at the end of each lesson in this workbook. There, we'll give you surprising statistics, helpful suggestions, and words of encouragement just for military families.

We are proud of you, we are praying for you, and we're prepared to stand beside you as you fight a different kind of battle—a battle to take control of your money. This course will give you the tools you need to win—*and win big.*

We appreciate the sacrifices you are making, and with all of the sincerity at our command, we thank you. God bless you.

—Dave Ramsey

Super Saving

Common Sense for Your Dollars and Cents

The Seven Baby Steps

There is a process for getting out of the mess that we created without feeling overwhelmed. Getting out of debt will not happen overnight; it takes time. Here are the Baby Steps that will get you started:

Step 1: $1,000 in an emergency fund
($500 if your income is under $20,000 per year)

Step 2:   Pay off all debt except the house utilizing the debt snowball (found in the Dumping Debt lesson)

Step 3:   Three to six months expenses in savings

Step 4:   Invest 15% of your household income into Roth IRAs and pre-tax retirement plans

Step 5:   College funding

Step 6:   Pay off your home early

Step 7:   Build wealth and give!

If you will live like no one else,
later you can live like no one else.

Baby Step 1 ™

$_____ in the bank.

If your income is under $20,000, make this $_____.

• Saving must become a _____.

• You must pay yourself _____.

• Give, save, then pay _____.

• Saving money is about _____ and _____.

• Building wealth is not evil or wrong. Money is _____.

• Larry Burkett, a famous Christian author, said, "The only difference in saving and hoarding is _____."

You should save for three basic reasons:

NOTES

1. _____ _____

2. _____

3. _____ _____

Emergency Fund

_____ events do occur—expect them!

Remember: Baby Step 1, a beginner emergency fund, is $_____ in the bank (or $500 if your household income is below $20,000 per year).

Baby Step 3 ™

___ to ___ months of expenses in savings.

A great place to keep your emergency fund is in a _____ _____ account from a mutual fund company.

Your emergency fund is not an _____;
it is _____.

Do not _____ this fund for purchases.

The emergency fund is your _____ savings priority. Do it quickly!

Purchases

Instead of _____ to purchase, pay cash by using
a _____ fund approach.

For example...
Say you borrow to purchase a $ _____ dining room set.
Most furniture stores will sell their financing contracts to
finance companies.

This means you will have borrowed at _____%
with payments of $_____ per month for _____ months.
So, you will pay a total of $_____, plus insurance, for that set.

But if you save the same $_____ per month for only _____
months, you will be able to pay cash.

When you pay cash, you can almost always negotiate a discount,
so you will be able to buy it even earlier.

"If you would be wealthy, think of saving as well as getting."

– Benjamin Franklin

"Today there are three kinds of people: the haves, the have-nots, and the have-not-paid-for-what-they-haves."

– Earl Wilson

One definition of maturity is learning to delay pleasure. Children do what feels good; adults devise a plan and follow it.

NOTES

Save for a $4,600 car by putting $_____ per month in the cookie jar for only 10 months!

Since we have pledged to borrow no more, this is the only way to make a purchase.

If your teenager really got this lesson early and **never** had a car payment throughout his whole life, do you realize how wealthy he could become just from this **one decision?**

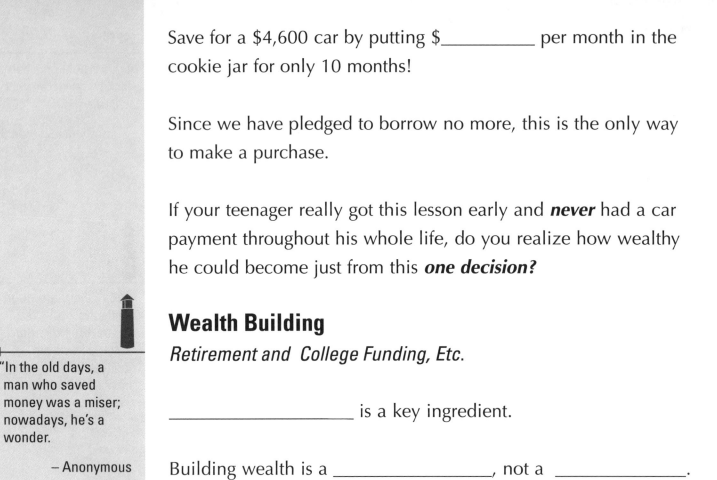

Wealth Building
Retirement and College Funding, Etc.

_____ is a key ingredient.

Building wealth is a _____, not a _____.

Just $_____ per month, every month, from age 25 to age 65, at _____% will build to over $_____.

"No discipline seems pleasant at the time, but painful. Later on, however, it produces a harvest of righteousness and peace for those who have been trained by it." – Hebrews 12:11 (NIV)

_____ _____ (PACs) withdrawals are a good way to build in discipline.

Compound interest is a mathematical _____.

You must start _____ !

"Self-confidence is the first requisite to great undertakings."

– Samuel Johnson

You will either learn to manage money, or the lack of it will always manage you.

Daily decisions can make a HUGE impact!

Expense	Cost per day	Cost per month	If invested at 12% from age 16-76
Cigarettes	$3	$90	$11,622,000
Gourmet Coffee	$5	$150	$19,371,943
Lunch (5 days/week)	$8	$160	$20,663,319

Is it worth the cost in the long run?

NOTES

The Story of Ben and Arthur

Both save $2,000 per year at 12%. Ben starts at age 19 and stops at age 26, while Arthur starts at age 27 and stops at age 65.

Age	Ben Invests:		Arthur Invests:	
19	2,000	2,240	0	0
20	2,000	4,749	0	0
21	2,000	7,558	0	0
22	2,000	10,706	0	0
23	2,000	14,230	0	0
24	2,000	18,178	0	0
25	2,000	22,599	0	0
26	2,000	27,551	0	0
27	0	30,857	2,000	2,240
28	0	34,560	2,000	4,749
29	0	38,708	2,000	7,558
30	0	43,352	2,000	10,706
31	0	48,554	2,000	14,230
32	0	54,381	2,000	18,178
33	0	60,907	2,000	22,599
34	0	68,216	2,000	27,551
35	0	76,802	2,000	33,097
36	0	85,570	2,000	39,309
37	0	95,383	2,000	46,266
38	0	107,339	2,000	54,058
39	0	120,220	2,000	62,785
40	0	134,646	2,000	72,559
41	0	150,804	2,000	83,506
42	0	168,900	2,000	95,767
43	0	189,168	2,000	109,499
44	0	211,869	2,000	124,879
45	0	237,293	2,000	142,104
46	0	265,768	2,000	161,396
47	0	297,660	2,000	183,004
48	0	333,379	2,000	207,204
49	0	373,385	2,000	234,308
50	0	418,191	2,000	264,665
51	0	468,374	2,000	298,665
52	0	524,579	2,000	336,745
53	0	587,528	2,000	379,394
54	0	658,032	2,000	427,161
55	0	736,995	2,000	480,660
56	0	825,435	2,000	540,579
57	0	924,487	2,000	607,688
58	0	1,035,425	2,000	682,851
59	0	1,159,676	2,000	767,033
60	0	1,298,837	2,000	861,317
61	0	1,454,698	2,000	966,915
62	0	1,629,261	2,000	1,085,185
63	0	1,824,773	2,000	1,217,647
64	0	2,043,746	2,000	1,366,005
65	0	*2,288,996*	2,000	*1,532,166*

Saving only $167 a month!

$2,288,996

With only a $16,000 investment!

$1,532,166

Arthur NEVER caught up!

What do we learn from Ben and Arthur?

Rate of return, or _____ rate, is important.

A simple, one-time investment of $1,000 could make a huge difference at retirement...if you know how and where to invest it.

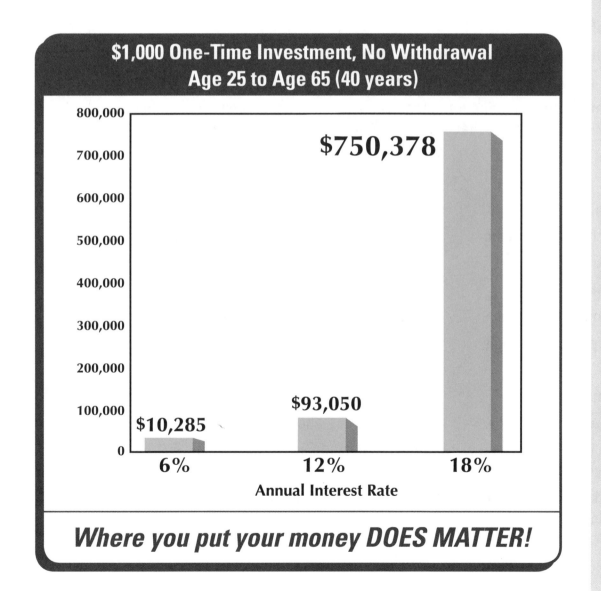

$1,000 One-Time Investment, No Withdrawal
Age 25 to Age 65 (40 years)

$750,378

$93,050

$10,285

6% 12% 18%

Annual Interest Rate

Where you put your money DOES MATTER!

"Make all you can,
save all you can,
give all you can."

– John Wesley

NOTES

The Basic Quickie Budget (Instructions)

This form will help you get your feet wet in the area of budgeting. It is only one page and should not be intimidating as you get started. The purpose of this form is to show you exactly how much money you need every month in order to survive. We won't get into the details of your credit card bills, student loans, and other consumer debts here. *This is just to give you a starting point as you begin to take control of your money.* You will learn how to create a full monthly cash flow plan in the third class session.

There are four columns on this form:

1. **Monthly Total**

   - This column shows you how much you are spending on necessities each month.

   - If you do not know the amount, write down your best estimate.

   - If an estimate is grossly inaccurate, then you may have never even noticed how much you were spending in that area before now. Don't beat yourself up about this!

2. **Payoff Total**

   - Write down how much money is required to completely pay off that item.

   - This line only appears in the relevant categories (mortgage, car debt, etc.).

3. **How Far Behind?**

   - If your account is past due in any category, write down how many days you are behind.

   - If you are up-to-date, simply write a zero or N/A (not applicable) here.

4. **Type of Account**

   - Write in how this area is paid—by check, automatic bank draft, cash, etc.

   - Early in the FPM course, you will see the benefits of using cash for certain items. Challenge yourself by identifying categories for which you can use cash only.

   - The asterisks (*) on the form indicate areas in which a cash-based approach could be helpful.

The Basic Quickie Budget

Item	Monthly Total	Payoff Total	How Far Behind	Type of Account
GIVING	$366		NA	Check
SAVING	$100		NA	Bank Draft
HOUSING				
First Mortgage	$915	$125,000	NA	Bank Draft
Second Mortgage				
Repairs/Mn. Fee				
UTILITIES				
Electricity	$100		NA	Check
Water	$55		NA	Check
Gas	$75		NA	Check
Phone	$45		NA	Check
Trash				
Cable	$21		NA	Check
*Food	$360		NA	Cash
TRANSPORTATION				
Car Payment	$400	$8,500	2 months	Check
Car Payment				
*Gas & Oil	$200		NA	Cash
*Repairs & Tires				
Car Insurance	$80		NA	Check
*CLOTHING	$100		NA	Cash
PERSONAL				
Disability Ins.				
Health Insurance	$300		NA	Bank Draft
Life Insurance				
Child Care				
*Entertainment	$200		NA	Cash
OTHER MISC.				

TOTAL MONTHLY NECESSITIES $3,317

Listen Up!
Special Insights for Military Families

- According to the Military Family Research Institute, 56% of enlisted military personnel report difficulty with family finances. In fact, 47% admitted to being in "over their heads" with their own expenses.

- The Department of Defense reports that financial issues account for approximately 80% of security clearance revocations. In fact, there was recently a 1,600% increase in the number of security clearances revoked or denied during a single five-year period.

So What?

The story of Ben and Arthur in this lesson teaches one extremely important point about saving: you must start NOW! Regardless of your age or income, saving money must be a priority. A military salary often represents the first regular income in a servicemember's life. Make it count by establishing good money habits early!

One way to do this is to "save the raise." That is, establish a solid, manageable budget with your current salary, and maintain that budget as you get pay raises for cost of living, longevity, promotions, and so on. Instead of blowing a raise on a new car or expensive toys, save it! Then, you'll be covered for emergencies, or have the cash on hand for major purchases later on.

One great way to save is to take advantage of the military's Savings Deposit Program. This plan allows servicemembers in a combat zone to contribute all or part of their pay—up to $10,000—in a special savings account that earns a guaranteed 10% annual interest rate.

Welcome and Introductions

Before starting this lesson's discussion, get to know the other members in your class. Going around the circle, you should take 1–2 minutes to share:

1. Who you are,

2. Why you're here, and

3. What you hope to get out of this program.

Small Group Discussion and Accountability

Respond to the following discussion questions, sharing openly and giving personal illustrations when possible. Be honest and *real* with each other.

1. What is keeping you from saving?

2. What is Baby Step 1? Why is this important?

3. Why do so many people use debt (credit cards, loans, etc.) for emergencies? Have you ever done this? Be honest!

4. Dave talked about how money is amoral, using the analogy of the brick. What did this illustration mean to you? Have you ever thought of money as being "good" or "bad" in and of itself?

5. What does "Murphy Repellent" mean? If you had some savings built up, do you think you'd have fewer emergencies?

6. Statistics show that most of us will have a major, unexpected, negative financial event in any 10-year period. What would constitute a "negative financial event" in your situation? How would you handle that today?

7. How would it feel if you had savings to cover an emergency? How would that change your attitude when unexpected things happen?

8. What would a fully funded emergency fund mean for your family during a deployment?

Homework

Get your FPM experience off to a great start by completing these crucial tasks this week:

Complete the Basic Quickie Budget form and *bring this to the next class.*
This is available in the forms section at the back of this workbook or online at daveramsey.com/mil-tools.

SUPER SAVING

ANSWER KEY

$1,000	First
$500	Borrowing
Priority	Sinking
First	$4,000
Bills	24%
Emotion	$211
Contentment	24
Amoral	$5,064
Attitude	$211
Emergency	18
Fund	$464
Purchases	Discipline
Wealth	Marathon
Building	Sprint
Unexpected	$100
$1,000	12%
3	$1,176,000
6	Pre-Authorized
Money	Checking
Market	Explosion
Investment	Now
Insurance	Interest
Touch	

Ethan
Grandson

Logan
Grandson

Cassidy
Granddaughter

Michaela
Granddaughter

Michelle
Daughter-in-law

Micah
Son-in-Law

Brandi
Daughter

Shannon
Son

Mom

Dad

Our Family Tree

Relating With Money™

Nerds and Free Spirits Unite!

Brandi
Daughter

Micah
Son-in-Law

Michelle
Daughter-in-law

Shannon
Son

Mom   Dad

Men, Women, and Money (over-generalizing)

The flow of money in a family represents the _____ _____ under which that family operates.

Emergency Fund Savings:

- Men: "It's boring and not _____ enough."

- Women: "It's the most _____ key to our financial plan."

Shopping:

- Men get good deals by _____.

- Men want to win.

- Women get good deals by _____.

- Women enjoy the process.

Financial Problems:

- Men lose _____ - _____ because money usually represents a _____ to them.

- Women face _____ or even _____ because, with women, money usually represents _____.

Marriage and Money

Can We Talk?

• The number one cause of divorce in America
  is _____ _____.

• When you agree on your value system, you will reach a
  _____ in your marriage that you can experience
  no other way.

Who Does the Financial Decision-Making?

• _____ of you!

• The partner with the natural _____ can prepare
  the _____, but the decision-making must be
  done by _____.

• The _____ likes doing the budget because it gives them
  control, and they feel like they are taking care of loved ones.

• The _____ _____ feels controlled, not cared
  for, and can appear irresponsible to the nerd.

NOTES

Brandi
Daughter

Micah
Son-in-Law

Michelle
Daughter-in-law

Shannon
Son

Mom   Dad

Singles and Money

- _____ _____ and fatigue can lead to poor money management.

- Beware of _____ buying, which can be brought on by _____ or even by the "I owe it to _____" syndrome.

- A written plan gives the single person _____, self-accountability, and _____.

Prevention

- Develop an _____ relationship.

   This is someone with whom to discuss major _____.

   This is someone with whom to discuss your _____.

- Accountability friends must love you enough to be brutally honest and promise to do so for your own good.

Suggested possibilities: pastoral staff, parent, relative, boss, etc.

Kids and Money

- Teaching your kids how to handle money is not the _____ responsibility. It is _____ responsibility!

- Pay _____, not allowance; we have enough people in our society who expect to be made allowance for.

- Words are _____.

- If you _____, you get paid; if you do not _____, you do not get paid.

- Teach by _____.

- Show them how you live _____ free, how insurance works, how an IRA works, etc.

Be Age-Appropriate

- If the children are young, use a clear _____ to save. Visual reinforcement is powerful.

- Use three envelopes for ages 5-12: _____, _____, and _____.

- Somewhere around 13-15 years old, open a _____ _____ for the child and teach him/her how to run it by monthly reviews.

> "Train up a child in the way he should go, and when he is old he will not depart from it. The rich rules over the poor, and the borrower is servant to the lender." – Proverbs 22:6-7 (NKJV)

"Tell me, and I'll forget. Show me, and I may not remember. Involve me, and I'll understand."

– Native American Saying

"Criticize the performance, not the performer."

– Anonymous

"When you put faith, hope, and love together, you can raise positive kids in a negative world."

– Zig Ziglar

NOTES

Brandi
Daughter

Micah
Son-in-Law

Michelle
Daughter-in-law

Shannon
Son

Mom   Dad

Listen Up!
Special Insights for Military Families

- Approximately one-third of all active-duty servicemembers are stationed outside the United States and are therefore thousands of miles away from their families.

- Research shows that about 20% of marriages end in divorce within two years of a spouse's deployment into a war zone.

- A 2008 survey by Defense Manpower Data Center found that 55% of military spouses reported a problem managing expenses and bills during a servicemember's deployment, with 32% describing the problems as "significant."

- This same study found that 17% of military spouses were faced with major financial hardship, up to and including bankruptcy, while their deployed spouses were away.

So What?

More servicemembers are married today than ever before, with a full one-third of first-term personnel leaving a spouse at home. Having a loving husband or wife back home is an enormous blessing, but it brings with it certain responsibilities that you simply cannot afford to ignore.

Repeated deployments take a toll on family life. Experts believe organizations that require high levels of responsibility, coupled with possible traumatic events and danger, have high levels of divorce. In fact, divorce currently affects 4.4% of active duty officers (below the rank of General) and 7.1% of enlisted men and women.

Sadly, this is not surprising. Military families often struggle with repeated moves, long separations, and inadequate housing. When financial mismanagement is thrown into the mix, the existing tensions and stressors can grow out of control.

Don't let this happen to your family! Take charge of your money by working together as a team, following the guidelines and principles in this lesson. Then, you'll be better equipped to face the trials of separation without the extra burden of money fights.

daveramsey.com/mil-tools

Review of Last Lesson

1. Name three reasons why you should save money.

2. What is Baby Step 1? Why is it important to do this first?

3. What can you do to fund your emergency fund quickly?

4. Everyone hold up your completed Basic Quickie Budget form. We told you we'd check to see if you did it!

Class Commitments

1. Make a verbal commitment to start putting something aside for an emergency fund every month, even if it is only $4.

2. Commit to attend every class session.

Small Group Discussion and Accountability

1. What are the advantages to being single in regards to financial control? What are the disadvantages?

2. What are some of the reasons that finances should be agreed upon by both partners in a marriage?

3. Do you put relationships above money, making your spouse, children, and friends more important than financial stress? Would others agree with your answer?

4. What are some practical ways to teach your kids about money?

5. Respond to this statement: "How you spend your money tells me who you are and what is important to you."

6. How does your military service affect the budgeting process? How can you overcome these challenges?

7. How will having a budget and emergency fund affect your PCS, TDY, or deployment?

Homework

1. **Start collecting credit card offers.** Keep track of all of the credit card offers that come in the mail throughout the rest of FPM. At the end of the class, we'll total everyone's offers up and see how much potential debt we've avoided throughout the class!

2. **Select an accountability partner.**

online resources ™

Take advantage of your online toolkit!
Download PDF and audio files of this week's lesson for review at anytime.

You can also download all of the budget forms to keep you on track.

Bonus Lessons:
Go online to enjoy extra lessons that are only available in your online toolkit.

RELATING WITH MONEY

ANSWER KEY

Value	Impulse
System	Stress
Sophisticated	Myself
Important	Empowerment
Negotiating	Control
Hunting	Accountability
Self	Purchases
Esteem	Budget
Scorecard	School's
Fear	Your
Terror	Commissions
Security	Powerful
Money	Work
Fights	Work
Unity	Example
Both	Debt
Gift	Container
Budget	Giving
Both	Spending
Nerd	Saving
Free Spirit	Checking
Time	Account
Poverty	

Dave Ramsey's
Financial Peace
MILITARY EDITION

Cash Flow Planning™

The Nuts and Bolts of Budgeting

Budgeting Basics

Money is _____.

You must do a written _____ _____ plan every month.

You must also keep your checking account _____.

Overdrafts are a sign of _____ _____
and sloppy, lazy money habits.

Use _____ checks if necessary.

If not managed and made to behave, the _____ card and the
_____ card are certain to become budget busters.

- Keep up with your receipts and write them in your account register.
- Use your bank's online tools to keep a close eye on your spending.

Reasons We DON'T Do a Cash Flow Plan

• Most people hate the word "budget" for four reasons:

  1. It has a _____ _____ connotation.

  2. It has been used to _____ them.

  3. They've never had a budget that _____.

  4. Paralysis from _____ of what they will find.

• Cash flow plans do not work when you:

  1. _____ things _____.

  2. _____ your plan.

  3. Don't actually _____ it.

  4. Don't actually _____ on it.

Most adults are pretty good at budgeting—when they bother to do it on purpose.

Budgeting is not a method by which you make other *people* behave. Budgeting is a method by which you make *money* behave.

"People don't plan to fail, they fail to plan."

– Anonymous

Money flows *from* those who don't manage it and *to* those who do.

"To accomplish great things, we must dream as well as act. "

– Anatole France

NOTES

_____

_____

_____

_____

_____

Reasons We SHOULD Do a Cash Flow Plan

- A written plan removes the "management by _____" from your finances.

- Managed money goes _____.

- A written plan, if actually lived and agreed on, will remove many of the _____ _____ from your marriage.

- A written plan, if actually lived and agreed on, will remove much of the _____, _____, and _____ that may now be a part of buying necessities such as food or clothing.

- A written plan, if actually lived and agreed on, will remove many of the _____ from your life, consequently removing a lot of _____.

- A written plan, if actually lived and agreed on, will show if you are _____ in a certain area.

- The easiest and most powerful method is a _____- based plan using the _____ system.

How To Balance Your Checking Account

- Keep your account register current by subtracting checks, debit card purchases, and withdrawals and adding deposits as they're made to keep your account balanced correctly.

- Balance your checking account within 72 hours of receiving your bank statement or online once a month to make sure there aren't any mistakes.

- What do I need to balance my account?
  1. Your account register
  2. Your last bank statement (in print or online)
  3. A reconciliation sheet (located on the back of most statements)

- Where do I start?
  Start by putting check marks in your register for each of the checks, debit card purchases, and other withdrawals, as well as deposits included in your bank statement. Make an entry in your register for any bank service charges or interest paid.

Checking Account Register						
Check Number	Date	Fee	Transaction Description	Payment	Deposit	Balance $564.46
5671	8/12	X	One Stop Grocery	57.40		507.06
5672	8/14		Electric Company	101.00		406.06
	8/14		Paycheck		700.00	1106.06
5673	8/16		Telephone Company	50.00		1056.06
5674	8/19		One Stop Grocery	66.00		990.06
		X	Bank Service Charge	2.50		987.56

How To Balance Your Checking Account (continued)

- On the reconciliation sheet, list any checks, withdrawals, or other deductions that are in your register that are not on your bank statement and total the list.

- On the reconciliation sheet, list any deposits that are in your register but are not included on your bank statement. Total the list.

- Beginning with the ending balance from your bank statement, subtract the total withdrawals and add the total deposits that were not on your statement.

- Compare with your register balance. If they don't agree, double check your lists and re-add your register entries until you find the difference. If the numbers will not agree, you're probably missing a transaction in your register. Make sure every transaction on your statement has been recorded and try again. In some cases, you may need your bank's help in getting your register to balance if you haven't done it in a while.

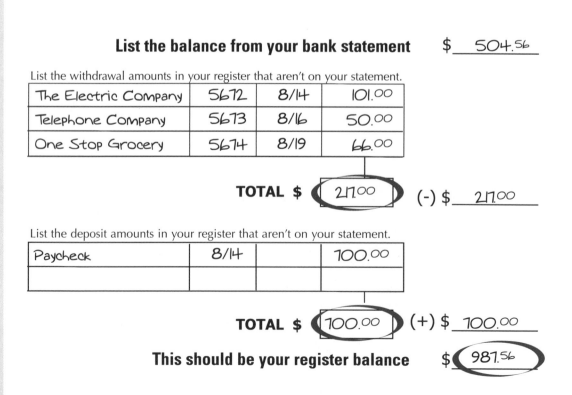

List the balance from your bank statement $ __504.56__

List the withdrawal amounts in your register that aren't on your statement.

The Electric Company	5672	8/14	101.00
Telephone Company	5673	8/16	50.00
One Stop Grocery	5674	8/19	66.00

TOTAL $ (217.00)   (-) $ __217.00__

List the deposit amounts in your register that aren't on your statement.

Paycheck		8/14	100.00

TOTAL $ (100.00)   (+) $ __100.00__

This should be your register balance $ (987.56)

34

Financial Management Forms

Welcome to the wonderful world of cash flow management! This level of detail may seem a bit intimidating at first, but don't worry—we'll walk you through this step by step.

By filling out just a few forms, your new financial plan will start to unfold right in front of you. You'll immediately identify problem areas and learn how to shut the valve of wasteful spending because you'll know exactly where all of your dollars are going!

The first time you fill out these forms, it will take a little while and you'll have to come face to face with the bad habits that have gotten you to this point. After that initial start-up, however, you'll get better and better until budgeting becomes second nature.

Complete the whole set of forms to get started. Then, you'll only need to do the "Monthly Cash Flow Plan" (Form 5), "Allocated Spending Plan" (Form 7), or the "Irregular Income Plan" (Form 8) once a month. Dave will teach you which form best fits your specific situation. This should only take about 30 minutes a month once you get in the habit.

You'll also want to update the whole set of forms once a year or whenever you experience a dramatic positive or negative financial event (such as receiving a large inheritance or paying for a major house repair).

Are you ready? Go for it!

Sample forms are provided here. The actual blank forms for you to use are found in the forms section at the back of this book.

All of these forms are also available for download. You can even do your monthly budget online with our powerful Gazelle Budget Software—FREE during your FPM class.

NOTES

Major Components of a Healthy Financial Plan (Form 1)

	Action Needed	Action Date
Written Cash Flow Plan	Complete first budget	NOW!
Will and/or Estate Plan	Make an appt. with lawyer	June 6
Debt Reduction Plan	Begin debt snowball	July 1
Tax Reduction Plan	NA	NA
Emergency Funding	On hold until Baby Step 3	NA
Retirement Funding	On hold until Baby Step 4	NA
College Funding	On hold until Baby Step 5	NA
Charitable Giving	Start tithing	June 15
Teach My Children	Get Financial Peace Jr.	August
Life Insurance	Done	NA
Health Insurance	Done	NA
Disability Insurance	Check company options	This week
Auto Insurance	Check current policy details	July 1
Homeowner's Insurance	Check replacement cost	This week

I (We) ___Joe & Suzie Public___, (a) responsible adult(s), do hereby promise to take the above stated actions by the above stated dates to financially secure the well-being of my (our) family and myself (ourselves).

Signed: ___Joe Q. Public___ Date: ___June 2___

Signed: ___Suzie Q. Public___ Date: ___June 2___

Consumer Equity Sheet (Form 2)

ITEM / DESCRIBE	VALUE	–	DEBT	=	EQUITY
Real Estate _____	$180,000		$149,000		$31,000
Real Estate _____					
Car _____	$2,500				$2,500
Car _____	$3,000				$3,000
Cash On Hand					
Checking Account					
Checking Account					
Savings Account	$1,600				$1,600
Money Market Account					
Mutual Funds					
Retirement Plan 1	$400				$400
Retirement Plan 2	$8,000				$8,000
Cash Value (Insurance)					
Household Items	$30,000				$30,000
Jewelry					
Antiques					
Boat					
Unsecured Debt (Neg)					
Credit Card Debt (Neg)					
Other _____					
Other _____					
Other _____					
TOTAL	$225,500		$149,000		$76,500

Income Sources (Form 3)

SOURCE	AMOUNT	PERIOD/DESCRIBE
Salary 1	$2,716	1st of Month
Salary 2	$945	1st & 15th – $472^{50}
Salary 3		
Bonus		
Self-Employment		
Interest Income		
Dividend Income		
Royalty Income		
Rents		
Notes		
Alimony		
Child Support		
AFDC		
Unemployment		
Social Security		
Pension		
Annuity		
Disability Income		
Cash Gifts		
Trust Fund		
Other_____		
Other_____		
Other_____		
TOTAL	$3,661	

Lump Sum Payment Planning (Form 4)

Payments you make on a non-monthly basis, such as insurance premiums and taxes, can be budget busters if you do not plan for them every month. Therefore, you must annualize the cost and convert these to monthly budget items. That way, you can save the money each month and will not be caught off-guard when your bi-monthly, quarterly, semi-annual, or annual bills come due. Simply divide the annual cost by 12 to determine the monthly amount you should save for each item.

ITEM NEEDED	ANNUAL AMOUNT		MONTHLY AMOUNT
Real Estate Taxes		/ 12 =	
Homeowner's Insurance		/ 12 =	
Home Repairs	$1,800	/ 12 =	$150
Replace Furniture		/ 12 =	
Medical Bills	$600	/ 12 =	$50
Health Insurance		/ 12 =	
Life Insurance		/ 12 =	
Disability Insurance		/ 12 =	
Car Insurance		/ 12 =	
Car Repair/Tags		/ 12 =	
Replace Car		/ 12 =	
Clothing		/ 12 =	
Tuition		/ 12 =	
Bank Note		/ 12 =	
IRS (Self-Employed)		/ 12 =	
Vacation	$1,200	/ 12 =	$100
Gifts (including Christmas)		/ 12 =	
Other _____		/ 12 =	

Monthly Cash Flow Plan (Form 5)

Budgeted Item	Sub Total	TOTAL	Actually Spent	% of Take Home Pay
CHARITABLE GIFTS		$366		10%
SAVING				
Emergency Fund	$224			
Retirement Fund				
College Fund		$224		6%
HOUSING				
First Mortgage	$915			
Second Mortgage				
Real Estate Taxes				
Homeowner's Ins.				
Repairs or Mn. Fee				
Replace Furniture	$50			
Other _____		$965		27%
UTILITIES				
Electricity	$100			
Water	$55			
Gas	$75			
Phone	$45			
Trash				
Cable	$21	$296		8%
*FOOD				
*Grocery	$360			
*Restaurants	$50	$410		12%
TRANSPORTATION				
Car Payment				
Car Payment				
*Gas and Oil	$150			
*Repairs and Tires				
Car Insurance	$80			
License and Taxes				
Car Replacement		$230		5%
PAGE 1 TOTAL		$2,491		

Monthly Cash Flow Plan (Form 5 – continued)

Budgeted Item	Sub Total	TOTAL	Actually Spent	% of Take Home Pay
*CLOTHING				
*Children	_____		_____	
*Adults	$100		_____	
*Cleaning/Laundry	_____	$100	_____	3%
MEDICAL/HEALTH				
Disability Insurance	_____		_____	
Health Insurance	$300		_____	
Doctor Bills	$50		_____	
Dentist	$20		_____	
Optometrist	_____		_____	
Medications	_____	$370	_____	10%
PERSONAL				
Life Insurance	$65		_____	
Child Care	_____		_____	
*Baby Sitter	_____		_____	
*Toiletries	_____		_____	
*Cosmetics	_____		_____	
*Hair Care	$60		_____	
Education/Adult	_____		_____	
School Tuition	_____		_____	
School Supplies	_____		_____	
Child Support	_____		_____	
Alimony	_____		_____	
Subscriptions	_____		_____	
Organization Dues	$25		_____	
Gifts (incl. Christmas)	_____		_____	
Miscellaneous	$50		_____	
*Pocket Money	$100	$300	_____	8%
PAGE 2 TOTAL		$770		

Monthly Cash Flow Plan (Form 5 – continued)

Budgeted Item	Sub Total	TOTAL	Actually Spent	% of Take Home Pay
RECREATION				
*Entertainment	$50			
Vacation	$25	$75		2%
DEBTS (Hopefully -0-)				
Visa 1	$100			
Visa 2				
Master Card 1	$75			
Master Card 2				
American Express	$50			
Discover Card				
Gas Card 1				
Gas Card 2				
Dept. Store Card 1				
Dept. Store Card 2				
Finance Co. 1				
Finance Co. 2				
Credit Line				
Student Loan 1	$100			
Student Loan 2				
Other _____				
Other _____				
Other _____				
Other _____				
Other _____		$325		9%
PAGE 3 TOTAL		$400		
PAGE 2 TOTAL		$770		
PAGE 1 TOTAL		$2,491		
GRAND TOTAL		$3661		
TOTAL HOUSEHOLD INCOME		$3661		
		ZERO		

Recommended Percentages (Form 6)

How much of your income should be spent on housing, giving, food, etc.? Through experience and research, we recommend the following percentages. However, you should remember that these are only *recommended* percentages. If you have an unusually high or low income, then these numbers could change dramatically. For example, if you have a high income, the *percentage* that is spent on food will be much lower than someone who earns half of that.

If you find that you spend much more in one category than we recommend, however, it may be necessary to adjust your lifestyle in that area in order to enjoy more freedom and flexibility across the board.

ITEM	ACTUAL %	RECOMMENDED %
CHARITABLE GIFTS	10%	10 – 15%
SAVING	6%	5 – 10%
HOUSING	27%	25 – 35%
UTILITIES	8%	5 – 10%
FOOD	12%	5 – 15%
TRANSPORTATION	5%	10 – 15%
CLOTHING	3%	2 – 7%
MEDICAL/HEALTH	10%	5 – 10%
PERSONAL	8%	5 – 10%
RECREATION	2%	5 – 10%
DEBTS	9%	5 – 10%

Allocated Spending Plan (Form 7)

PAY PERIOD:	7 / 1	7 / 8	7 / 15	7 / 22

ITEM:

INCOME	$3,188	0	$472	0

CHARITABLE	366 / 2822	___ / ___	___ / ___	___ / ___

SAVING

Emergency Fund	224 / 2598	___ / ___	___ / ___	___ / ___
Retirement Fund	___ / ___	___ / ___	___ / ___	___ / ___
College Fund	___ / ___	___ / ___	___ / ___	___ / ___

HOUSING

First Mortgage	915 / 1683	___ / ___	___ / ___	___ / ___
Second Mortgage	___ / ___	___ / ___	___ / ___	___ / ___
Real Estate Taxes	___ / ___	___ / ___	___ / ___	___ / ___
Homeowner's Ins.	___ / ___	___ / ___	___ / ___	___ / ___
Repairs or Mn. Fees	___ / ___	___ / ___	___ / ___	___ / ___
Replace Furniture	___ / ___	___ / ___	50 / 422	___ / ___
Other _____	___ / ___	___ / ___	___ / ___	___ / ___

UTILITIES

Electricity	100 / 1583	___ / ___	___ / ___	___ / ___
Water	___ / ___	___ / ___	55 / 367	___ / ___
Gas	___ / ___	___ / ___	15 / 292	___ / ___
Phone	45 / 1538	___ / ___	___ / ___	___ / ___
Trash	___ / ___	___ / ___	___ / ___	___ / ___
Cable	21 / 1517	___ / ___	___ / ___	___ / ___

*FOOD

*Grocery	200 / 1317	___ / ___	160 / 132	___ / ___
*Restaurants	25 / 1292	___ / ___	25 / 107	___ / ___

Allocated Spending Plan (Form 7 – continued)

TRANSPORTATION

Car Payment	___ / ___	___ / ___	___ / ___	___ / ___
Car Payment	___ / ___	___ / ___	___ / ___	___ / ___
*Gas and Oil	75 / 1217	___ / ___	75 / 32	___ / ___
*Repairs and Tires	___ / ___	___ / ___	___ / ___	___ / ___
Car Insurance	80 / 1137	___ / ___	___ / ___	___ / ___
License and Taxes	___ / ___	___ / ___	___ / ___	___ / ___
Car Replacement	___ / ___	___ / ___	___ / ___	___ / ___

*CLOTHING

*Children	___ / ___	___ / ___	___ / ___	___ / ___
*Adults	100 / 1031	___ / ___	___ / ___	___ / ___
*Cleaning/Laundry	___ / ___	___ / ___	___ / ___	___ / ___

MEDICAL/HEALTH

Disability Insurance	___ / ___	___ / ___	___ / ___	___ / ___
Health Insurance	300 / 737	___ / ___	___ / ___	___ / ___
Doctor	50 / 687	___ / ___	___ / ___	___ / ___
Dentist	___ / ___	___ / ___	20 / 12	___ / ___
Optometrist	___ / ___	___ / ___	___ / ___	___ / ___
Medications	___ / ___	___ / ___	___ / ___	___ / ___

PERSONAL

Life Insurance	65 / 622	___ / ___	___ / ___	___ / ___
Child Care	___ / ___	___ / ___	___ / ___	___ / ___
*Baby Sitter	___ / ___	___ / ___	___ / ___	___ / ___
*Toiletries	___ / ___	___ / ___	___ / ___	___ / ___
*Cosmetics	___ / ___	___ / ___	___ / ___	___ / ___
*Hair Care	___ / ___	___ / ___	___ / ___	___ / ___
Education/Adult	60 / 562	___ / ___	___ / ___	___ / ___
School Tuition	___ / ___	___ / ___	___ / ___	___ / ___
School Supplies	___ / ___	___ / ___	___ / ___	___ / ___
Child Support	___ / ___	___ / ___	___ / ___	___ / ___

Allocated Spending Plan (Form 7 – continued)

Alimony	___ / ___	___ / ___	___ / ___	___ / ___
Subscriptions	___ / ___	___ / ___	___ / ___	___ / ___
Organization Dues	25 / 531	___ / ___	___ / ___	___ / ___
Gifts (including Christmas)	___ / ___	___ / ___	___ / ___	___ / ___
Miscellaneous	50 / 481	___ / ___	___ / ___	___ / ___

*Pocket Money	100 / 381	___ / ___	___ / ___	___ / ___

RECREATION

*Entertainment	50 / 331	___ / ___	___ / ___	___ / ___
Vacation	25 / 312	___ / ___	___ / ___	___ / ___

DEBTS (Hopefully -0-)

Visa 1	100 / 212	___ / ___	___ / ___	___ / ___
Visa 2	___ / ___	___ / ___	___ / ___	___ / ___
MasterCard 1	75 / 137	___ / ___	___ / ___	___ / ___
MasterCard 2	___ / ___	___ / ___	___ / ___	___ / ___
American Express	50 / 81	___ / ___	___ / ___	___ / ___
Discover Card	___ / ___	___ / ___	___ / ___	___ / ___
Gas Card 1	___ / ___	___ / ___	___ / ___	___ / ___
Gas Card 2	___ / ___	___ / ___	___ / ___	___ / ___
Dept. Store Card 1	___ / ___	___ / ___	___ / ___	___ / ___
Dept. Store Card 2	___ / ___	___ / ___	___ / ___	___ / ___
Finance Co. 1	___ / ___	___ / ___	___ / ___	___ / ___
Finance Co. 2	___ / ___	___ / ___	___ / ___	___ / ___
Credit Line	___ / ___	___ / ___	___ / ___	___ / ___
Student Loan 1	81 / 0	___ / ___	12 / 0	___ / ___
Student Loan 2	___ / ___	___ / ___	___ / ___	___ / ___
Other _____	___ / ___	___ / ___	___ / ___	___ / ___
Other _____	___ / ___	___ / ___	___ / ___	___ / ___

Irregular Income Planning (Form 8)

Many people have an irregular income, which simply means that their compensation fluctuates from month to month. This is especially common for the self-employed, as well as commission-based salespeople. While this makes it more difficult to predict your income, you are still responsible for doing a monthly budget!

The Monthly Cash Flow Plan (Form 5) should remain a crucial part of your plan, as it lays out exactly how much money you need to bring home each month to survive and prosper. However, instead of doing the Allocated Spending Plan (Form 7), you will use this Irregular Income Planning sheet.

On this form, simply look at the individual items from your Monthly Cash Flow Plan sheet and prioritize them by importance. Ask yourself, "If I only have enough money to pay one thing, what would that be?" Put that at the top of your list. Then, ask yourself, "If I only have enough money to pay one more thing, what would that be?" That's number two. Keep this up all the way down the list.

With your list in place, you're ready to get paid. If you get a $1,500 paycheck, you will spend that $1,500 right down the list until it is gone, recording the cumulative amount spent in the Cumulative Amount column. At that point, you're finished spending, no matter what remains unpaid on the list. That's why the most important things are at the top of the list, right?

Be prepared to stand your ground. Things usually have a way of seeming *important* when they are only *urgent*. For example, a once-in-a-lifetime opportunity to see your favorite band perform live may seem *important*, but in reality, it is only *urgent*, meaning that it is time-sensitive. Urgency alone should not move an item to the top of this list!

Item	Amount	Cumulative Amount
JC Penney	$150	$150
Sears	$250	$400
Visa	$500	$900
Vacation – part	$200	$1100
Christmas	$400	$1500

Breakdown of Savings (Form 9)

After you have fully funded your emergency fund, you can start to save for other items, such as furniture, car replacement, home maintenance, or a vacation. This sheet will remind you that every dollar in your savings account is already committed to something. For example, it's a bad idea to take money away from car repairs to pay for an impulse Hawaiian vacation, even if you pay cash for it. What would you do if the car broke down the week you got back home? However, it can be okay to reassign the dollars to another category, as long as you do it on purpose and it doesn't put you in a pinch in another category. Keep up with your breakdown of savings every month, one quarter at a time.

Item		Balance By Month		
		October	November	December
Emergency Fund (1)	$1,000			
Emergency Fund (2)	3-6 months			
Retirement Fund				
College Fund				
Real Estate Taxes				
Homeowner's Insurance				
Repairs or Mn. Fee				
Replace Furniture				
Car Insurance				
Car Replacement		$600	$700	$800
Disability Insurance				
Health Insurance		$500	$500	$500
Doctor				
Dentist				
Optometrist				
Life Insurance				
School Tuition				
School Supplies				
Gifts (incl. Christmas)		$500	$650	$800
Vacation				
Other _____				
Other _____				
TOTAL		$1,600	$1,850	$2,100

Listen Up!
Special Insights for Military Families

- Every year, about one-third of all servicemembers make a permanent change of station (PCS) move.

- Servicemembers facing a PCS move should take advantage of the Military Assistance Program's Relocation Budget Planner.

- Servicemembers in a combat zone or hazardous duty area may be eligible for a 180-day extension on the April 15 tax deadline.

- Combat zone pay is not subject to income tax but may be claimed as taxable earned income under certain conditions, such as claiming the Child Tax Credit.

- Servicemembers may ask the IRS military-specific questions by emailing them at combatzone@irs.gov or calling 800.829.1040.

So What?

Military couples must sit down together to create a deployment action plan for home finances. As part of this plan:

- **Budget for the whole year.** Go ahead and lay out a reasonable plan that includes your family's goals over several months. This will adjust a bit each month, but it will provide a basic roadmap for the spouse back home.

- **Plan for extra expenses.** Be sure your plan includes funds for the extra expenses your spouse will face during the deployment, such as yard work, day care, and so on.

- **Create a "Legacy Box."** Collect all important information, such as wills, retirement plans, insurance policies, mortgage papers, and so on, in a single, well-organized file drawer. The ability to locate critical papers in an emergency will be an enormous source of security for the spouse at home.

Review of Last Lesson

1. The flow of money represents your family's:
   A. Income   B. Value System   C. Teamwork

2. Explain the concept of the Nerd and Free Spirit.

3. Who should do the financial decision-making in a marriage?

4. How can an accountability partner help a single person win with money?

Small Group Discussion and Accountability

1. What are the benefits of a written cash flow plan? Be specific. How can this impact a marriage? How can it strengthen a single person?

2. What things have kept you from living on a cash flow plan?

3. What are some reasons why you've always hated the idea of a budget? What are your initial reactions to the concept?

4. How can the concept of the Four Walls (food, shelter, clothing, transportation) empower you to prioritize vyour spending?

5. When have you been guilty of letting someone else set your family's financial priorities? Explain.

6. Why is it important to set aside a little "Pocket money" every month?

7. How would good budgeting habits help the spouse at home during a deployment? How would it help the servicemember while away from home?

8. Why is it important for an unmarried servicemember to maintain a monthly budget, even if his or her monthly expenses are minimal?

Homework

Create a full zero-based budget for your household this week, using either the Monthly Cash Flow Plan form or the online budgeting software. ***Remember to bring your budget to the next class session!***

online resources ™

daveramsey.com/mil-tools

Take advantage of your online toolkit!
Download PDF and audio files of this week's lesson for review at anytime.

You can also download all of the budget forms to keep you on track.

Bonus Lessons:
Go online to enjoy extra lessons that are only available in your online toolkit.

CASH FLOW PLANNING

Active	Overcomplicate
Cash	Do
Flow	Live
Balanced	Crisis
Crisis	Farther
Living	Money
Duplicate	Fights
ATM	Guilt
Debit	Shame
Straight	Fear
Jacket	Overdrafts
Abuse	Stress
Worked	Overspending
Fear	Zero
Leave	Envelope
Out	

Dumping Debt™

Breaking the Chains of Debt

Quick History of Plastic:

- The credit card was born in 1950.

- The Bank Americard and American Express were created in 1958.

- The VISA brand was established in 1976.

- Discover entered the scene in 1986.

Debunking the Myth

If you tell a lie or spread a _____ often enough, loud enough, and long enough, the myth becomes accepted as _____.

Debt has been _____ to us in so many forms and so aggressively since the 1960s that to even imagine living without it requires a complete _____ _____.

Myth: If I loan money to a friend or relative, I will be _____ them.

Truth: The relationship will be strained or _____.

Myth: By _____ a loan, I am helping out a friend or relative.

Truth: The bank requires a cosigner because the person isn't likely to _____. So, be ready to pay the loan and have your credit damaged because you are on the loan.

Myth: Cash advance, rent-to-own, title pawning, and tote-the-note car lots are needed _____ for lower income people to get ahead.

Truth: These are horrible, _____ rip-offs that are not needed and benefit no one but the owners of these companies.

Myth: Playing the lottery and other forms of gambling will make me _____.

Truth: The lottery is a tax on the poor and on people who can't do _____.

Myth: Car _____ are a way of life, and you'll always have one.

Truth: Staying away from car payments by driving reliable used cars is what the typical millionaire does. That is _____ they became millionaires.

If you do rich people stuff, you get rich.

If you do poor people stuff, you get poor.

It's really that simple.

NOTES

Myth: _____ your car is what sophisticated financial people do. You should always lease things that go down in value. There are tax advantages.

Truth: _Consumer Reports_, _Smart Money_ magazine, and a good calculator will tell you that the car lease is the most _____ way to finance and operate a vehicle.

Truth: If you own a business, you can write off your _____ car on taxes without paying payments for the privilege.

Truth: The way to minimize the money lost on things that go down in value is to buy slightly _____.

Myth: You can get a good deal on a _____ car.

Truth: A new car loses _____% of its value in the first four years. This is the largest purchase most consumers make that goes down in value.

Myth: I'll take out a 30-year mortgage and pay _____, I promise!

Truth: Life happens! Something else will always seem more important, so almost no one pays extra every month. Never take more than a _____ fixed-rate loan.

30 Year vs. 15 Year Mortgage at 6%

		PAYMENT	TOTAL	PAY BACK
Home Purchased	$250,000	30 years	$1,349	$485,636
Down Payment	$ 25,000	15 years	$1,899	$341,762
Mortgage Amount	$225,000	Difference	$ 550	$143,874

You Save More Than $143,000!

Myth: It is wise to take out an _____ or a _____ mortgage if "I know I'll be moving."

Truth: You will be moving when they _____.

NOTES

_____

_____

_____

_____

_____

Myth: You need a credit card to _____ a car or to make _____ online or by phone.

Truth: A _____ card will do all of that, except for a few major rental companies. Check in advance.

Myth: "I pay mine off every _____ with no annual fee. I get brownie points, air miles, and a free hat."

Truth: When you use plastic instead of cash, you spend _____% more because spending cash hurts. So what if you get 1% back and a free hat?

Myth: I'll make sure my _____ gets a credit card so he/she can learn to be responsible with money.

Truth: Teens are a huge _____ of credit card companies today.

Myth: The home equity loan is good for _____
and is a substitute for an emergency fund.

Truth: You don't go into _____ for emergencies.

Myth: Debt consolidation _____ interest, and you get just
one smaller payment.

Truth: Debt consolidation is a _____.

Truth: Debt consolidation typically saves _____
or _____ interest because you will throw your low
interest loans into the deal.

Truth: You can't _____ your way out of debt.

Truth: Smaller payments equal more _____ in debt.

Myth: Debt is a _____ and should be used to create prosperity.

Truth: The borrower is _____ to the lender.

Truth: When surveyed, the Forbes 400 were asked, "What is the most important key to building wealth?" _____% replied that becoming and staying debt free was the number one key to wealth building.

How much could you _____, invest, spend, and _____ if you had no payments?

Steps Out of Debt

1. Quit _____ more _____!

2. You must _____ money.

3. _____ really works.

4. _____ something.

5. Take a part-time _____ or _____ (temporarily).

Baby Step 2 ™

Pay off all debt using the _____ _____.

Credit Card Crumbs

- The total American consumer debt is more than $2.7 trillion.

- The average household credit card debt has increased approximately 167% in the past 17 years.

- There are over 1.3 billion credit cards in circulation in America.

- The credit card industry mails out over six billion credit card offers each year, sending an average of six offers a month to each American household.

- 45% of American cardholders make only the minimum payments on their consumer debt.

- The average balance per credit card-holding household is more than $9,300.

- It would take over 13 years to pay off the average credit card balance if only making minimum monthly payments of 4% at an average interest rate of 15%.

- Credit card interest rates are often raised when a cardholder takes out a new loan, such as a mortgage, car loan, or other type of credit account.

- A single, first offense late payment can immediately raise a cardholder's interest rate as high as 34%. A "late payment" is defined as anything that posts after 2:00 p.m. on the due date.

- In addition to increasing the cardholder's interest rate, a card issuer can charge a fee of typically $29-39 for a late payment.

- The credit card industry takes in $43 billion per year in additional, unexpected fees from the consumer, such as late payment, over-the-limit, and balance transfer fees. Late fees alone bring in more than $11 billion.

- Overall, American households spend over $412 billion in credit card charges each year.

NOTES

Debt Snowball (Instructions)

Now it's time to knock out that debt! List your debts in order, from the smallest balance to the largest. Don't be concerned with interest rates, unless two debts have a similar payoff balance. In that case, list the one with the higher interest rate first. As you start eliminating debts, you'll start to build some serious momentum. These quick wins will keep you motivated, so you'll be able to stay on track.

The idea of the snowball is simple: pay minimum payments on all of your debts except for the smallest one. Then, attack that one with gazelle intensity! Every extra dollar you can get your hands on should be thrown at that smallest debt until it is gone. Then, you attack the second one. Every time you pay a debt off, you add its old minimum payment to your next debt payments. So, as the snowball rolls over, it picks up more snow. Get it?

Redo this sheet every time you pay off a debt so that you can see how close you're getting to total debt freedom. Keep the old sheets for encouragement—or to wallpaper the bathroom in your debt-free house someday!

The New Payment is the total of the previous debt's payment PLUS the current debt's minimum. As these payments compound, you'll start making huge payments as you work down the list.

Debt Snowball (Form 10)

Item	Total Payoff	Minimum Payment	New Payment
JC Penney	$150	$15	(Garage Sale)
Sears	$250	$10	$25
Visa	$500	$75	$100
MasterCard	$1,500	$90	$190
Car	$4,000	$210	$400
Student Loan	$4,000	$65	$465

Listen Up!
Special Insights for Military Families

- The Department of Defense reports that 17% of military personnel use payday loans.

- Over 40% of military service personnel are under the age of 25 and are easy targets for predatory lenders.

- Rent-to-own comes with a price tag of 2–5 times greater than what the item would have cost if it had been bought outright.

- Military families are experiencing a disproportionate increase in foreclosure rates compared to the general population. In the first quarter of 2008, the number of U.S. homes in foreclosure rose 59%, compared to a 217% increase among military homeowners during that same period.

So What?

Payday lenders, rent-to-own stores, and title pawn shops line up at the entrance to military installations. These establishments prey on servicemembers and offer quick fixes—at unbelievably bad terms and conditions.

Before the DoD regulated out-of-control interest rates for these establishments, the average payday interest rate was 400%.

Here's a real-world example of why payday loans are such a nightmare: The average payday loan is around $325. On top of that, there is a fee of about $52 and a ridiculous interest rate. Under these conditions, the average borrower would stay in debt to the payday lender for over seven months and eventually repay $1,105 for that $325 loan.

This trap is destroying servicemembers all over the country. Do not fall for it!

Review of Last Lesson

1. What is a zero-based budget? Why is it important?

2. Name one of the reasons we need to do a zero-based budget each month.

3. Hold up your budget! How did your first family budget session go?

Small Group Discussion and Accountability

1. How old were you when you got your first credit card? How did that make you feel (at the time)?

2. What wovvl like to have absolutely no debt?

3. Think about all the money that is currently going out in the form of debt payments (credit cards, furniture, car loan, mortgage, etc.). What could you do with all that money every month if you actually got to keep it?

4. Do you currently have or have you ever had a debt CONsolidation loan? Did you discover that it really was a con?

5. Have you ever believed or spread any of the myths covered in this lesson? Which ones?

6. Why is "gazelle intensity" so important in getting out of debt?

7. What is your reaction to the phrase, "the borrower is *slave* to the lender"?

8. How would your Commander or First Sergeant react if you requested permission to take on a part-time job for extra income?

9. Have you noticed an unusual concentration of title-pawn and cash-advance businesses around your installation? If so, why do you think that is?

Homework

1. **Complete the Credit Card History form** and use it as a guide as you start to close those accounts as soon as possible.

2. **Complete your Debt Snowball form** and get ready to dump your debt! ***Bring this form to the next class session.*** This is available in the forms section at the back of this workbook or online at daveramsey.com/mil-tools.

DUMPING DEBT

ANSWER KEY

Myth	Debit
Truth	Month
Marketed	12-18%
Paradigm	Teenager
Shift	Target
Helping	Consolidation
Destroyed	Debt
Co-signing	Saves
Repay	Con
Services	Little
Greedy	No
Rich	Borrow
Math	Time
Payments	Tool
How	Slave
Leasing	75%
Expensive	Save
Paid-For	Give
Used	Borrowing
New	Money
70%	Save
Extra	Prayer
15-Year	Sell
ARM	Job
Balloon	Overtime
Foreclose	Debt
Rent	Snowball
Purchases	

Dave Ramsey's
Financial Peace
MILITARY EDITION

Credit Sharks In Suits

Understanding Credit Bureaus & Collection Practices

Credit Score

One more myth...

Myth: You need to take out a credit card or car loan to "build up your _____ _____."

Truth: The FICO score is an "I love _____" score and is not a measure of _____ financially.

Credit Bureaus

Account information is removed from your credit report _____ years after the last activity on that account, except for a Chapter 7 bankruptcy, which stays on for _____ years.

Beware of credit clean-up scams. The only information that may be legally removed from a credit report is _____ information.

The National Association of State Public Interest Research Groups (U.S. PIRG) did a survey of 200 adults in 30 states who checked their credit report for accuracy.

- _____% of those credit reports contained mistakes of some kind and _____% of them contained errors serious enough to result in the denial of credit.

- _____% of the credit reports contained credit accounts that had been closed by the consumer but incorrectly remained listed as open.

- _____% listed the same mortgage or loan twice.

You should check your credit report _____, which you can now do for free.

Identity Theft

What To Do:

1. Place a _____ _____ alert on your credit bureau report (stays on for 90 days without a police report).

2. Get a _____ _____.

3. Remember, this is _____. You owe _____ and should pay _____.

4. Contact the fraud victim _____ of each creditor and furnish _____.

5. Be _____ — this will take some time. You now have a new _____.

Of all the identity theft victims who call in to *The Dave Ramsey Show* for help and advice on this subject, approximately one-half know the person who stole their identities. The thief is often a friend or a family member.

_____ **NOT**

_____

_____

_____

Correcting Credit Report Inaccuracies

An updated version of the 1977 Federal Fair Credit Reporting Act requires a credit bureau to _____ all inaccuracies within 30 days of notification of such inaccuracies.

To clean your credit report of inaccurate information, you should write a separate letter for each inaccuracy, staple a copy of your credit report to each letter, and circle the account number.

Note: You should also request that "inquiries" be removed. All of these letters should be sent _____ mail with return receipt requested to prove when they receive the letter. If the credit bureau does not prove the accuracy of the account within 30 days, you should request they remove the _____ account from your file.

You will have to be assertive after the 30-day period.

Lodge any _____ with the Federal Trade Commission and your state's Consumer Affairs Division.

Collection Practices

- The best way to pay debts is with a _____.

- A collector's job is not to help your overall situation. His only job is to get your _____.

- Collectors are trained _____ or _____.

- They are typically low-paid positions with high _____.

- They are taught in their training to evoke strong _____.

- The way to counteract this technique is to ALWAYS pay _____ first, and then _____ set the order of payment.

"If you think nobody cares if you're alive, try missing a couple of car payments."

–Earl Wilson

"Be kinder than necessary, for everyone you meet is fighting some kind of battle."

– Anonymous

NOTES

_____

_____

_____

_____

Federal Fair Debt Collection Practices Act

In 1977, a consumer law was passed by Congress called the Federal Fair Debt Collection Practices Act to protect you from unfair collectors. The law technically only applies to collection agencies (not your creditor), but later court cases make most creditors also abide by the FFDCPA.

- The Act states that harassment is illegal, and restricts a collector's calls between the hours of _____ and _____ (unless they have your permission).

- The Act also allows you to demand that a creditor cease calling you at _____. You should request this in writing by certified mail with return receipt requested.

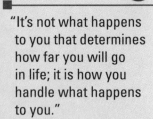
- The Act even allows you to insist that a creditor stop _____ contact except to notify you of _____ proceedings.

- Do not use a cease-and-desist letter except in horrible situations, because all _____ stop and any hope of a positive resolution is lost.

- No collector or creditor may _____ a bank account or garnish (attach) _____ without proper and lengthy court action, except in the case of delinquent IRS or student loan debt. All such threats are a bluff.

Pro Rata Plan

Your plan should include as much prompt repayment of debt as possible, but YOU must set your priorities of repayment. Do NOT let a collector use your credit report as a

_____ _____.

When you are unable to pay the minimum payments, use the _____ _____ plan.

"I've never been poor, only broke. Being poor is a frame of mind. Being broke is only a temporary position."

– Mike Todd

"A light purse is a heavy curse."

– Benjamin Franklin

Always set your priorities by the Four Walls:

1. Food   3. Clothing
2. Shelter   4. Transportation

NOTES

Pro Rata Debts (Instructions)

Pro rata means the fair share, or the percent of your total debt each creditor represents. This will determine how much you should send them when you cannot make the minimum payments. Even if you cannot pay your creditors what they request, you should pay everyone as much as you can. Send the check for their pro rata share, along with a copy of your budget and this form, every month. *Do this even if the creditor says they will not accept it.*

Do you need to use the pro rata plan?

First, use your monthly cash flow plan to determine your total disposable income. Simply write down your income on the line at the top of the form. Then, write down the total you spend on necessities (not including consumer debt) each month. Subtract the necessity expense from the income, and you are left with your disposable income. This is the money you have to put toward your debts.

Second, add up your total amount of debt, not including your home, and write that in the blank provided. Below that, write in the total of the minimum monthly payments on all your debts. If the total of your minimum payments is greater than your total disposable income, you need to use the pro rata plan.

For example, Joe and Suzie have a total debt of $2,000, with a combined total minimum payment of $310. However, this family only has $200 in disposable income each month, which means they do not have enough money to make the minimum payments. So, they will use the pro rata plan to give each creditor their fair share of the family's $200.

How to Use This Form

This form has six columns:
1. **Item:** the name and type of the account.
2. **Total Payoff:** the total amount due on the account.
3. **Total Debt:** the combined total of all your debts.
4. **Percent:** the portion of the total debt load that each account represents. You can calculate this by simply dividing the Total Payoff by the Total Debt for each line.
5. **Disposable Income:** the amount of money you have left after paying necessities.
6. **New Payment:** the amount that you will now send to each creditor. You calculate this by multiplying the numbers in each line's Percent and Disposable Income columns.

The pro rata plan helps you to meet your obligations to the best of your ability. Of course, your creditors will not like receiving less than their required minimum payments. However, if you keep sending them checks, they'll most likely keep cashing them. We have had clients use this plan, even when sending only $2, who have survived for years.

Pro Rata Debt List (Form 11)

Income _____ $3361 _____

Necessity Expense − _____ $3161 _____

Disposable Income = _____ $200 _____

Total Debt:	$2,000
Total Minimum Payments:	$310

Item	Total Payoff		Total Debt		Percent		Disposable Income		New Payment
J.C. Penney	100	/	2,000	=	5% (.05)	X	200	=	$10
Sears	200	/	2,000	=	10% (.10)	X	200	=	$20
MBNA Visa	200	/	2,000	=	10% (.10)	X	200	=	$20
CitiBank Visa	300	/	2,000	=	15% (.15)	X	200	=	$30
Discover	1,200	/	2,000	=	60% (.60)	X	200	=	$120
		/		=		X		=	
		/		=		X		=	
		/		=		X		=	
		/		=		X		=	
		/		=		X		=	
		/		=		X		=	
		/		=		X		=	
		/		=		X		=	
		/		=		X		=	
		/		=		X		=	
		/		=		X		=	
		/		=		X		=	
		/		=		X		=	
		/		=		X		=	

Lawsuits

Eventually, if you are making no payments and have cut no deals, you will get sued.

Typically, lawsuits for under $_____ are filed in General Sessions Court (or small claims court), which is a fairly informal proceeding.

Before you are sued, you will be served by the local sheriff's department and typically given _____ days notice of the court date.

In court, if the debt is valid, even if you fight, you will _____. From that date you will generally have 30 days before the _____ becomes final and garnishments or attachments begin.

At ANY TIME during the process, you may settle with the creditor or their attorney in writing. If you are not able to reach an agreement, you can file with the court a "_____ _____ motion," called a "pauper's oath" in some states.

"Creditors have better memories than debtors."

– Benjamin Franklin

Facts You Should Know

- Payment history on your credit file is supplied by credit grantors with whom you have credit. This includes both open accounts and accounts that have already been closed.

- Payment in full does not remove your payment history. The length of time information remains on file is:

  Credit and collection accounts – Seven years, plus 180 days, from the date of the original delinquency.

  Courthouse records – Seven years from the date filed, except bankruptcy Chapters 7 and 11, which remain for 10 years from date filed.

- A divorce decree does not supersede the original contract with the creditor and does not release you from legal responsibility on any accounts. You must contact each creditor individually and seek their legally binding release of your obligation. Only after that release can your credit history be updated accordingly.

- There may appear to be duplicate accounts reported in your credit file. This could be because some credit grantors issue both revolving and installment accounts. Another reason is that when you move, some credit grantors transfer your account to a different location and issue another account number.

- The balance reported is the balance on the date the source reported the information. Credit grantors supply information on a periodic basis, so the balance shown may not be the balance you know it is today. If the balance reported was correct as of the date reported, it is not necessary to reinvestigate the balance on that account.

NOTES

Credit Bureaus

The FACT Act amendments to the Fair Credit Reporting Act require the nationwide credit bureaus to provide consumers, upon request, one free personal credit report in any 12-month period. You may contact the Central Source online at www.annualcreditreport.com or by calling toll free (877) FACT ACT. Free copies are also available if you have been denied credit in the past 60 days and the creditor used their services.

- EXPERIAN
  Phone: (888) 397-3742
  Website: www.experian.com

- EQUIFAX CREDIT BUREAU
  Phone: (800) 685-1111
  Website: www.equifax.com

- TRANSUNION CREDIT BUREAU
  Phone: (877) 322-8228
  Website: www.transunion.com

- FEDERAL TRADE COMMISSION
  Phone: (202) 326-2222
  Address: 600 Pennsylvania Avenue, N.W.
                  Washington, D.C. 20580
  Website: www.ftc.gov

  Publishes a brief, semi-annual list (March and September) on card pricing by the largest issuers for $5 per copy. Offers a number of free credit-related publications.

Be Proactive

Decrease unauthorized direct mail marketing (including pre-approved credit card offers) and unwanted telemarketing calls!

- PRE-SCREENING OPT OUT
  Phone: (888) 567-8688
  Website: www.optoutprescreen.com

- NATIONAL DO NOT CALL REGISTRY
  Phone: (888) 382-1222
  Website: www.donotcall.gov

Direct Marketing Association

For detailed information on your rights and options regarding direct marketing, visit the Direct Marketing Association's website. They have great resources to help educate consumers on how direct marketing works, how to stay off mailing and phone lists, and more!

Visit www.dmachoice.org for details.

NOTES

Request For File Disclosure Form

REQUEST FOR FILE DISCLOSURE

CREDIT BUREAU OF NASHVILLE

604 FOURTH AVE NORTH - P.O. BOX 190589 - NASHVILLE, TN 37219-0589

Reason for File Disclosure Request _____

Referred by _____ Was credit refused?   yes   no

I hereby request the Credit Bureau of Nashville to disclose to me the contents of my credit record. I understand that if I have been rejected for credit within the past sixty (60) days as the result of credit information contained in my credit record, there will be NO CHARGE for this disclosure, otherwise there will be an $8 charge for an individual disclosure or $10 for both myself and my spouse.

Name _____ Phone No. _____

Spouse's Name _____

Present Address _____

City _____, State _____ Zip Code _____

Former Address _____

City _____, State _____ Zip Code _____

Date of Birth _____ Social Security No. _____

Employed By _____

How Long? _____ Position _____

Former Employment _____

Spouse's Date of Birth _____ Social Security No. _____

Spouse's Employment _____

How Long? _____ Position _____

I hereby authorize the Credit Bureau of Nashville to review my credit record with me, to make any necessary investigation of my credit transactions and to furnish to its subscribers reports based thereon. In consideration of its undertaking to make such an investigation I authorize any business or organization to give full information and records about me.

I am the person named above and I understand that federal law provides that a person who obtains information from a consumer reporting agency under false pretenses shall be fined not more than $5,000 or imprisoned no more than one year or both.

Signed _____ Date _____

Telephone Number _____ Ext _____ where I can be reached during normal working hours.

AUTHORIZATION FOR DISCLOSURE OF SPOUSE'S CREDIT RECORD
I, _____, certify that I am presently married to _____, and am acting in his/her behalf in reviewing the credit record information concerning him/her maintained by the Credit Bureau of Nashville.

Sample Removal Letter

Date _____

(From)

_____

_____

_____

VIA: Certified Mail, Return Receipt Requested

(To)
Mail Preference Service
Direct Marketing Association
P.O. Box 282
Carmel, NY 10512

RE: Unauthorized direct marketing and pre-approved credit card offers

This letter is your formal notice to remove my name from all direct marketing and pre-screening databases. I do not wish to receive any unsolicited offers, especially from credit card companies.

Not only do I request that my name be permanently removed, but I also request that my phone number and address must likewise be permanently removed. My correct information is as follows:

      (Complete Name)

      (Full Address)

      (Phone Number with Area Code)

Thank you for your immediate attention to this matter.

Sincerely,

(Signatures)

Sample Cease and Desist Letter

Date _____

(From)

_____
_____
_____

VIA: Certified Mail, Return Receipt Requested
(To)

_____
_____
_____

RE: _____

Dear _____,

You are hereby notified under provisions of Public Law 95-109, Section 805-C, the FAIR DEBT COLLECTION PRACTICES ACT to CEASE AND DESIST in any and all attempts to collect the above debt.

Your failure to do so WILL result in charges being filed against you with the state and federal regulatory agencies empowered with enforcement.

Please be further warned that if ANY derogatory information is placed on any credit reports after receipt of this notice, that too will result in action being taken against you.

PLEASE GIVE THIS MATTER YOUR IMMEDIATE ATTENTION.

Sincerely,

_____
(Signature)

Sample Credit Bureau Letter

Date _____

(From)

_____
_____
_____

(To)

_____
_____
_____

RE: _____

In reviewing the attached credit bureau report issued by your agency, I have detected an error. The following account(s) is/are reported inaccurately:

Company Name:_____
Account Number: _____

Under the provisions of the 1977 Federal Fair Credit Reporting Act, I hereby request that your agency prove to me in writing the accuracy of the reporting of this account. Under the terms of the Act and succeeding court cases, you have 30 days to prove such accuracy or remove the account entirely from my report. I ask that you do so.

This letter was sent certified mail, return receipt requested. I expect a response within the 30-day period. Should I not hear promptly from you, I will follow up with whatever action necessary to cause my report to be corrected.

Please feel free to call me if you have any questions. My home phone number is _____, and my office number is _____.

Sincerely,

_____
(Signature)

Sample Creditor Letter

Date _____

(From)

_____

_____

_____

(To)

_____

_____

_____

RE: _____

Dear _____,

I am writing to formally request that, in accordance with the 1977 Federal Fair Debt Collection Practices Act, your firm (or any agency hired by your firm) no longer contact me at my place of employment, _____.

Please take note that this letter was mailed certified mail, return receipt requested, so that I will have proof that you are in receipt of this letter should legal action against you become necessary.

I am willing to pay the debt I owe you, and I will be in touch soon to work out arrangements.

Feel free to contact me at my home between _____ a.m. and _____ p.m. at the following number: _____, or by mail at my home address: _____.

Please give this matter your immediate attention.

Sincerely,

_____

(Signature)

Sample Pro Rata Plan Letter

Date: February 22, 2006

From: Joe and Suzie Public
    123 Anystreet
    Anytown, ST 11111

To: Mega Credit Card Company
    999 Main Street
    Big City, ST 00000

Re: Joe and Suzie Public # 1234-5678-9012-9999

Dear Collection Manager:

Recently I lost my job. My wife is employed in a clerical position. We have met with a financial counselor to assess our present situation.

We acknowledge our indebtedness to you of $6,000 and fully intend to pay you back in full. However, you are one of six creditors to whom we owe a total of $42,968. We owe minimum payments of $782 each month. We are not able to meet these minimum payments at the present time, and we will not go further into debt to meet these obligations.

We have put together a cash flow plan based on our take-home pay of $2,340 per month (see the enclosed copy of cash flow plan). Since we have two small children and no disposable income, we cannot make a payment to you at the present time, but we do not intend to go bankrupt.

We are asking for a moratorium on payments for the next 120 days. We will keep in close contact with you, and as soon as possible, we will begin making payments. If possible, we further request a reduction in interest during this time.

We are aware that this is an inconvenience to you, but we must meet the basic needs of our family first. We fully intend to pay our creditors all that we owe them. Please be patient with us. If you have any questions please contact us at 600-555-9876.

Thank you for your consideration of our present situation.

Sincerely,

Joe Public
Suzie Public

Listen Up!
Special Insights for Military Families

- The military takes debt even more seriously than bill collectors do. Under military law, servicemembers can be—and often are—discharged for excessive financial irresponsibility.

- According to a 2007 California task force report, the number of U.S. Navy discharges due to debt increased a whopping 903% between 2000 and 2005.

- Collectors are not the only credit sharks looking for a bite out of your wallet. Banks also get in on the action through over-the-top fees and penalties. They actually *want* you to bounce checks or overdraft your account with your debit card. A $100 overdraft for two weeks with a $20 fee has an APR of 520%.

So What?

The military equates financial readiness with mission readiness, and nothing can distract a servicemember from doing his or her job like collections pressure back home. This is even worse for those who know their spouses are getting collector calls every day and yet can't be there to help.

If you or your family is in this situation, learn the rules for communicating with collectors in this lesson, and apply them to every call, every time. Make a plan for repayment and stick to it.

If you currently have debt but the phone isn't ringing yet, dump that debt as soon as possible! You and your family have enough things to worry about. Don't allow the threat of future collections pressure to stay on the list.

Review of Last Lesson

1. What are the six steps to getting out of debt?

2. What are the seven Baby Steps (in order)?

3. Why is it important to complete Baby Step 1 before moving on to Baby Step 2?

Small Group Discussion and Accountability

1. For those of you who have been contacted by a collector or creditor, what emotions have you experienced?

2. Has anyone's spouse been pressured by a collector while you were away on a deployment? How did it make you feel to know that was happening back home?

3. In what way is *emotion* a collector's best weapon?

4. Have you ever let a collector set your family's priorities?

5. What are the "Four Walls"? Why is it important to always pay necessities first before paying your creditors, such as credit card companies?

6. True or False: A collector can garnish your wages at any time.

7. Has anyone here been a victim of identify theft? How has that impacted your life?

8. Does your military service make you more or less likely to receive collections pressure?

Homework

1. **Review your credit report.** You can get a free copy from each of the three credit agencies once a year. Check it for accuracy immediately!

2. **Cut up the credit cards!** Still clinging to your plastic? Bring them to the next class and chop them to pieces!

online resources

Take advantage of your online toolkit!
Download PDF and audio files of this week's lesson for review at anytime.

You can also download all of the budget forms to keep you on track.

Bonus Lessons:
Go online to enjoy extra lessons that are only available in your online toolkit.

daveramsey.com/mil-tools

CREDIT SHARKS IN SUITS

ANSWER KEY

Credit	Plan
Score	Money
Debt	Salespeople
Winning	Telemarketers
7	Turnover
10	Emotion
Inaccurate	Necessities
79%	You
25%	8:00 a.m.
30%	9:00 p.m.
22%	Work
Annually	All
Fraud	Lawsuit
Victim	Negotiations
Police	Take
Report	Wages
Theft	Paper
Nothing	Club
Nothing	Pro
Division	Rata
Documentation	$10,000
Persistent	10
Hobby	Lose
Remove	Judgment
Certified	Slow
Entire	Pay
Complaints	

Buyer Beware™

The Power of Marketing on Your Buying Decisions

Caveat Emptor (Let The Buyer Beware)

Profile of the Enemy

(The enemy of your Financial Peace)

Companies use every angle to aggressively compete for your _____.

Four Major Ways:

1. _____ selling

2. _____ as a marketing tool

   • _____% of 90 days same-as-cash contracts convert to payments which are usually at _____% APR with Rule of 78's prepayment penalty.

3. _____, _____, _____, and other media

4. Product _____

   ✓ Brand Recognition   ✓ Shelf Position

   ✓ Color   ✓ Packaging

Significant Purchases

A "significant purchase" is normally anything over $_____.
Our bodies go through physiological _____ when making
a significant purchase.

We all have that spoiled, red-faced, grocery store kid living
inside of us. His name is _____.

What To Do

Because you can always spend more than you _____, you
must develop a power over _____ by:

1. Waiting _____ before making a purchase.

2. Carefully considering your buying _____. No
   amount of _____ equals contentment or fulfillment.

3. Never buying anything you do not _____.

4. Considering the "_____ _____" of your money.

5. Seeking the _____ of your spouse.

NOTES

Listen Up!
Special Insights for Military Families

- Deployed servicemembers should place an "active duty alert" on their credit reports. This protects against identity theft by requiring businesses to verify the individual's identity before issuing any credit.

- The Servicemembers Civil Relief Act (SCRA) provides many protections for all servicemembers, including active, Reserve, and active-duty National Guard. Specific coverage includes:

  - Protection against credit card debt, mortgage payments, pending trials, taxes, rising interest rates, and lease terminations under certain circumstances.

  - Protection against home eviction from leased properties due to nonpayment while on active duty, as long as the monthly rent is no more than $2,932.31 per month (as of 2009), adjusted annually.

  - Ability to terminate a housing lease due to a PCS or a deployment of over 90 days.

  - Interest rate lock at 6% for debts incurred prior to activation.

  - Ability to terminate a car lease without penalty upon deployment or PCS for 180 days or more.

So What?

The SCRA was designed with the unique needs of military families in mind. Even if only one or two specific points of the SCRA apply to your financial situation, this could save you hundreds of dollars and help secure your family's home during a deployment.

Talk to your installation's legal office to see how the SCRA applies to you.

Review of Last Lesson

1. What are collectors trained to do?

2. Who should set the priorities for your family—
you or the collectors?

3. How often should you check your credit report? Why?

4. What are the Four Walls?

5. Name the seven Baby Steps in order.

Small Group Discussion and Accountability

1. How do marketers use emotion to compel you to purchase their goods?

2. As a servicemember, do you feel especially targeted by marketers?

3. How can waiting overnight before making a purchase change your behavior? Would you have as much debt now if you had always waited overnight?

4. How would you define a "major purchase"? Why is it so important for married couples to agree on major purchases?

5. What can singles do to guard themselves against impulsive buying decisions?

6. How can you ensure that you will genuinely enjoy your purchases?

7. True or False: I do not borrow money anymore, including using credit cards. Why or why not?

8. In what ways has having an accountability partner been helpful to you? Do you still need help in this area?

Homework

Memorize the five keys to gaining power over your purchases and make yourself accountable to someone for following these principles for every major purchase.

online resources ™

daveramsey.com/mil-tools

Take advantage of your online toolkit!
Download PDF and audio files of this week's lesson for review at anytime.

You can also download all of the budget forms to keep you on track.

Bonus Lessons:
Go online to enjoy extra lessons that are only available in your online toolkit.

BUYER BEWARE

ANSWER KEY

Money
Personal
Financing
88%
24%
TV
Radio
Internet
Positioning
$300
Changes
Immaturity
Make
Purchase
Overnight
Motives
Stuff
Understand
Opportunity
Cost
Counsel

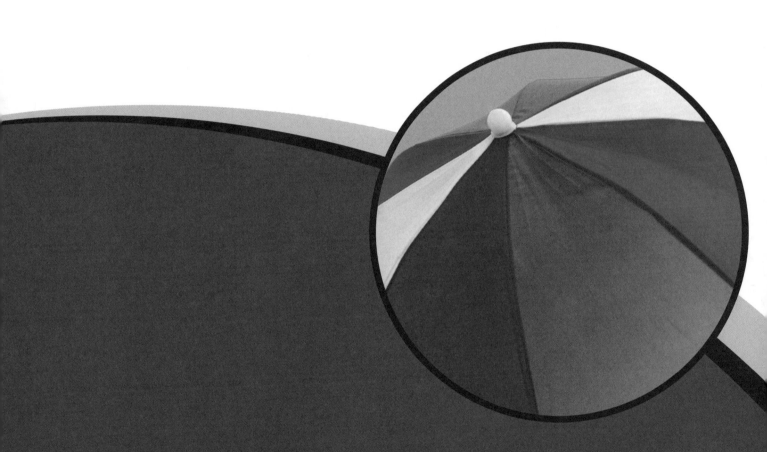

Clause and Effect™

The Role of Insurance in Your Financial Plan

Understanding Insurance

Insurance is an essential financial planning tool.

The purpose of insurance is to _____ risk.

Without proper insurance, certain losses can _____ you. Conventional wisdom says that you should transfer that risk.

Basic Types of Coverage Needed

1. Homeowner's or Renter's Insurance
2. Auto Insurance
3. Health Insurance
4. Disability Insurance
5. Long-Term Care Insurance
6. Identity Theft Protection
7. Life Insurance

Do a break-even analysis to see if raising your deductible makes sense. Compare your annual premium savings with a higher deductible to the extra risk you would take on in the event of an accident.

Types of Insurance

- **Homeowner's and Auto Insurance**

  If you have a full emergency fund, raise your _____.

  Carry adequate _____.

  Consider dropping your _____ on older cars.

  Homeowner's insurance should be "guaranteed _____ cost."

  _____ liability policies are a good buy once you have some assets.

- **Health Insurance**

  Keys to saving on your health premiums:

  Increase your _____ and/or coinsurance amount.

  Increase your_____-_____, but never decrease your maximum pay.

  See if an _____, a Health Savings Account, would make sense for your situation.

  The HSA is a _____-_____ savings account for medical expenses that works with a high deductible insurance policy.

NOTES

Disability insurance is
a long-term solution.
Your short-term needs
should be covered by
a full emergency fund
of three to six months
of expenses.

- **Disability Insurance**

  Disability insurance is designed to replace _____ lost due to a short-term or permanent disability.

  Try to buy disability insurance that pays if you cannot perform the job that you were educated or _____ to do.

  That is called _____, or "own occ," disability. Many times, this is only available for two years.

  Beware of _____-term policies covering less than _____ years.

  Your coverage should be for _____% of your current income.

  The _____ period is the time between the disabling event and when the payments actually begin.

  A _____ elimination period will _____ your premium cost.

Even if it's not time to
get long-term care
insurance for yourself,
you may need to have
this discussion with
your parents.

- **Long-Term Care Insurance**

  Long-term care insurance is for _____ home, assisted living facilities, or in-home care.

  _____% of people over the age of 65 will require long-term care at some point in their lives.

98

- **Identity Theft Protection**

  Don't buy ID theft protection that only provides credit report _____.

  Good protection includes _____ services that assign a _____ to clean up the mess.

- **Life Insurance**

  Life insurance is to replace lost income due to _____.

  Most people have no _____ what kind of life insurance they _____.

Two Types of Life Insurance:

1. _____ insurance is for a specified period, is substantially cheaper, and has no savings plan built into it.

2. _____ _____ insurance is normally for life and is more expensive because it funds a savings plan.

The most common insurance myth is that the need for life insurance is a _____ situation.

Twenty years from today, when the children are grown and gone, you are debt free (including that 15-year mortgage), and you have investments that have grown to a substantial amount, you will have become self-_____.

Human beings have a 100% mortality rate—we're all going to die someday. If people depend on your income, it is your responsibility to make sure they'll be taken care of if something were to happen to you.

"It is unwise to hope for the best without preparing for the worst."

– Anonymous

"For what is your life? It is even a vapor that appears for a little time and then vanishes away."

– James 4:14 (NKJV)

NOTES

99

Why Not Life Insurance as an Investment?

1. Returns are historically _____.

2. When you die with cash value, the insurance company _____ the cash value.

3. The _____ deducted from your return are extremely _____.

Cash Value vs. Term + Roth IRA

For $145 a month, you could have $125,000 in cash value insurance. Or, for that same $145, you could pay $10 for $400,000 in 20-year term insurance *and* invest $135 into a Roth IRA. If you start at age 30...

Age	$125,000 Cash Value Guaranteed	$135/mo in Roth 12% Return
50	$27,500	$133,000
70	$66,000	$1,500,000

Before You Cancel Your Cash Value Policy...

Make sure that you already have a new term policy in place! If, for some reason, you cannot be approved for a new term policy, it is better to hang on to a bad cash value policy than to have nothing at all—*until you become self-insured.*

What To Remember When Purchasing Life Insurance

1. Buy only low-cost level _____.

2. Do not forget your _____.

3. Stay away from fancy _____.

4. Children only need enough for _____ expenses.

You need about _____ times your income. Invested at 10-12%, the annual interest would replace your lost income.

Insurance to Avoid

1. _____ life and disability

2. Credit _____ protection

3. _____ and hospital indemnity

4. Accidental _____

5. Any insurance with _____ _____, investments, or refund

6. Pre-paid _____ policies

7. _____ life insurance

8. Any kind of _____ coverage

A stay-at-home mom brings enormous economic value to a home. If something were to happen to her, dad would need the money to replace part of what mom does.

Listen Up!
Special Insights for Military Families

Health Insurance

- Tricare, the DoD's health care program, offers Tricare Prime HMO, Tricare Extra PPO, and Tricare Standard fee-for-service. Make sure you understand the benefits of each option as you make a selection.

- A family member's key to Tricare eligibility depends on enrollment in the Defense Enrollment Eligibility Reporting System (DEERS). Servicemembers should be certain that their family's information always remains current in DEERS.

- Not all hospitals accept Tricare. Reservists and Guard members and their families may be better off staying on employer-sponsored health plans while on active duty, if possible.

- Learn more about Tricare's plans and eligibility at www.tricare.mil.

Life Insurance

- Servicemembers' Group Life Insurance (SGLI) term life is available to all active duty servicemembers up to $400,000. Spouses can be covered up to $100,000. SGLI is terminated when the servicemember leaves the military.

- The SCRA protects servicemembers' privately purchased life insurance policies from termination due to nonpayment while on active duty, as long as the policy was in place at least 180 days before military service. Also, premium payments can be deferred for the length of their service, but must be repaid within two years of discharge.

- Learn more about your health and life insurance options at the VA's website, www.va.gov.

So What?

The proper types and amounts of insurance are vital to every adult—especially those in hazardous careers and/or those with family members depending on their income. If you do not have the proper insurance in place, be sure to create an action plan to correct this oversight this week!

Review of Last Lesson

1. Name five keys to power over purchase. Did you discuss these things with your spouse or accountability partner this week?

2. Complete this statement: "FPM has helped my life by...."

Small Group Discussion and Accountability

1. What do you do if money is tight?

    A. Drop your insurance until you've paid off your debts.

    B. Put insurance only on the person who brings home the most income and pray nothing happens to the rest of the family.

    C. Make insurance a priority to avoid a financial disaster.

2. What could happen to you financially if you do not have the proper amount of insurance in place?

3. How does having an emergency fund affect your insurance premiums and deductibles?

4. What is the difference between term and cash value life insurance?

5. What happens to your cash savings inside of a cash value life insurance plan when you die?

6. Why is it so important to make sure your homeowner's policy includes guaranteed replacement cost?

7. Why do you think so few people carry long-term disability coverage? Why is this so dangerous?

8. Discuss some military-specific options, such as SGLI, SBP, and the DIC program. Do you have any experience with these options?

Homework

1. **Complete the Insurance Coverage Recap form** in the back of this book. Make sure your spouse or other beneficiaries know where to locate this form in an emergency. This is also available in the forms section at the back of this workbook or online at daveramsey.com/mil-tools.

2. **Identify any insurance policies** that need to be changed or added to your financial plan.

3. **Calculate how much life insurance coverage you need** based on Dave's principles.

online resources

daveramsey.com/mil-tools

Take advantage of your online toolkit!
Download PDF and audio files of this week's lesson for review at anytime.

You can also download all of the budget forms to keep you on track.

Bonus Lessons:
Go online to enjoy extra lessons that are only available in your online toolkit.

CLAUSE AND EFFECT

ANSWER KEY

Transfer	Idea
Bankrupt	Own
Deductible	Term
Liability	Cash
Collision	Value
Replacement	Permanent
Umbrella	Insured
Deductible	Low
Stop-Loss	Keeps
HSA	Fees
Tax-Sheltered	High
Income	Term
Trained	Spouse
Occupational	Options
Short	Burial
5	10
65%	Credit
Elimination	Card
Longer	Cancer
Lower	Death
Nursing	Cash
69%	Value
Monitoring	Burial
Restoration	Mortgage
Counselor	Duplicate
Death	

From Fruition To Tuition™

Planning for Retirement and College

Retirement and College Funding

Once the emergency fund is in place, you should begin retirement and college funding, which falls within long-term investing for _____.

> ## Baby Step 4
>
> # Invest ___% of your household income into Roth IRAs and pre-tax retirement plans.

ALWAYS save long-term with tax -_____ dollars.

Tax-favored means that the investment is in a _____ _____ or has special tax treatment.

Qualified Plans
- Individual Retirement Arrangement (IRA)
- Simplified Employee Pension Plan (SEPP)
- 401(k), 403(b), 457

Individual Retirement Arrangement (IRA)

- Everyone with an _____ income is eligible.

- The maximum annual contribution for income earners and non-income producing spouses is $_____ as of 2008.

- Remember: IRA is not a type of _____ at a bank. It is the *tax treatment* on virtually any type of investment.

Roth IRA

The Roth IRA is an _____-tax IRA that grows
tax -_____!

If you _____ like we teach, you should use the Roth IRA.

Who is eligible?
- Singles – 100% contribution with income less than $95,000. Phase out between $95,000-$110,000 income. Not eligible above $110,000.

- Married filing jointly – 100% contribution with income less than $150,000. Phase out between $150,000-$160,000. Not eligible over $160,000.

Why the Roth IRA?
1. More _____.
2. Higher _____ at retirement.
3. More _____.
4. More _____.

The Roth IRA is named for Senator William Roth (R-Delaware), who authored this section of the Taxpayer Relief Act of 1997.

NOTES

Flexibility:

- Tax-free and penalty-free withdrawals at any time equal to contributions. After the emergency fund is depleted, you have a fall back.

- After five years, you can make tax-free, penalty-free withdrawals of 100% under these conditions:

    1. Over 59 and a half years old
    2. Because of death or disability
    3. First-time home purchase (max $10,000)

Simplified Employee Pension Plan (SEP)

A _____-employed person may deduct up to _____% of their net profit on the business by investing in a SEP.

- The maximum deductible amount is $45,000 (as of 2007) and all employees who have been with the firm more than three of the last five years must receive the same percentage of their pay.

401(k), 403(b) & 457 Retirement Plans

Most companies have completely done away with traditional _____ plans in the last 10-20 years. Some new plans offer a variety of pre-tax choices.

Some companies are now offering the _____ 401(k), which grows tax-free.

Do not use a Guaranteed Investment _____ (GIC) or bond funds to fund your plan.

You should be funding your plan whether your company _____ or not, but the plans that have company matching provide even greater returns.

Rollovers

You should _____ roll all retirement plans to an IRA when you _____ the company.

Do not bring the money home!
Make it a _____ _____.

You should roll to a Roth IRA ONLY if:

1. You will have saved over $_____ by age 65.

2. You pay your taxes _____ of _____ and not from the IRA funds.

3. You understand that all taxes will become due on the rollover amount.

"There's not a lot you can do about the national economy, but there is a lot you can do about your personal economy."

– Zig Ziglar

Currently, you can only roll an IRA to a Roth IRA if you make LESS than $100,000. This restriction may expire in 2010, in which case you could roll to a Roth regardless of your income.

NOTES

Borrowing against your retirement plan is a bad move. Even though you pay yourself back some interest, it is nowhere close to what you would have earned if you had left the money in the investment. Plus, if you leave the company or die before it is repaid, you or your heirs will have 60 days to pay it back in full or you will be hit with enormous penalties and interest. Don't do it!

Need some advice as you start investing?

Find someone in your area who has the heart of a teacher. Never let an advisor make your financial decisions for you. Their job is to teach you how to make *your own* decisions.

Retirement Loans

Never _____ against your retirement plan.

Federal Thrift Plan

If you are a federal government worker and have the standard thrift plan, we recommend _____% in the C Fund, _____% in the S Fund, and _____% in the I Fund.

Our Suggestion

How to fund your 15%:

1. Fund 401(k) or other employer plans up to the _____ (if applicable).

2. Above the matched amount, fund _____ IRAs. If there is no match, start with Roth IRAs.

3. Complete 15% of your income by going back to your _____ or other company plans.

Note: This is the best plan if you end up with $700,000 or more by age 65, because mandatory retirement withdrawals will cause a higher tax bracket at retirement.

Imagine if...

A 30-year-old couple partially funds a Roth IRA
($500 per month) at 12%. At 70 years old they will have...

$5,882,386 — TAX FREE!

Imagine if...

That same 30-year-old couple made $40,000 and saved 15% in a
401(k) ($500 per month) at 12%. At 70 years old they will have...

$5,882,386 in the 401(k).

By Retirement

That 30-year-old couple, DEBT FREE, saves $1,000 per month at
12%. At 70 years old, they will have:

Roth IRA	**$5,882,386**
401(k)	**$5,882,386**
Total	**$11,764,772**

This could be you if you get serious
about savings and investments!

Baby Step 5 ™

Save for your children's _____ using tax-favored plans.

First...

Save in an Education Savings Account (ESA), or "Education _____."

- You may save $2,000 (after tax) per year, per child, that grows tax free! So, if you start when your child is born and save $2,000 a year for 18 years, you would only invest a total of $36,000. However, at 12% growth, your child would have $126,000 for college—TAX FREE!

Above that...

If you want to save more or if you don't meet the income limits for an ESA, use a certain type of _____ plan.

- The only type we recommend is one that leaves _____ in control of the mutual fund at all times.

- Never buy a plan that:
  1. _____ your options.
  2. Automatically changes your investments based on the _____ of the child.

Only then...

Move to an _____ or _____ plan.

- While this is one way to save with reduced taxes, it is _____ as good as the other options.

- UTMA/UGMA stands for Uniform _____ / Gift to Minors Act.

- The account is _____ in the child's name and a _____ is named, usually the parent or grandparent. This person is the manager until the child reaches age 21. At age 21 (age 18 for UGMA), they can do with it what they please.

Three "Nevers" of College Saving

1. Never save for college using _____.

2. Never save for college using _____ bonds. (Only earns 5-6%)

3. Never save for college using _____ college tuition. (Only earns 7% inflation rate)

Monthly Retirement Planning (Form 12)

Too many people use the READY-FIRE-AIM approach to retirement planning. That's a bad plan. You need to aim first. Your assignment is to determine how much per month you should be saving at 12% interest in order to retire at 65 with the amount you need.

If you save at 12% and inflation is at 4%, then you are moving ahead of inflation at a net of 8% per year. If you invest your nest egg at retirement at 12% and want to break even with 4% inflation, you will be living on 8% income.

Step 1: Annual income (today) you wish to retire on: ___50,000___

Divide by .08

(Nest egg needed) equals: ___625,000___

Step 2: To achieve that nest egg you will save at 12%, netting 8% after inflation. So, we will target that nest egg using 8%.

		8% Factors (select the one that matches your age)		

Nest Egg Needed $ ___625,000___

Multiply by Factor   X ___.000436___

Monthly Savings Needed = ___$272.^{50}___

Your Age	Years to Save	Factor
25	40	.000286
30	35	.000436
35	30	.000671
40	25	.001051
45	20	.001698
50	15	.002890
55	10	.005466
60	5	.013610

Note: Be sure to try one or two examples if you wait 5 or 10 years to start.

Monthly College Planning (Form 13)

In order to have enough for college, you must aim at something. Your assignment is to determine how much per month you should be saving at 12% interest in order to have enough for college.

If you save at 12% and inflation is at 4%, then you are moving ahead of inflation at a net of 8% per year.

Step 1:   In today's dollars, the annual cost of the college of your choice is:

Amount per year $ ___20,000___

X 4 years = $ ___80,000___

(hint: $15,000 to $25,000 annually)

Step 2:   To achieve that college nest egg, you will save at 12%, netting 8% after inflation. So, we will target that nest egg using 8%.

Nest Egg Needed $ ___80,000___

Multiply by Factor   X ___.003287___

Monthly Savings Needed   = ___$262.⁹⁶___

Note: Be sure to try one or two examples if you wait 5 or 10 years to start.

8% Factors (select the one that matches your child's age)		
Child's Age	Years to Save	Factor
0	18	.002083
2	16	.002583
4	14	.003247
6	12	.004158
8	10	.005466
10	8	.007470
12	6	.010867
14	4	.017746

Listen Up!
Special Insights for Military Families

- The 6% SCRA interest rate cap does not apply to student loans. However, the Department of Education often postpones student loan payments for Reservists on active duty. Servicemembers should ask the school administrator or visit www.nasfaa.org for more details.

- Military members enrolled in the Post-9/11 G.I. Bill program may now transfer unused educational benefits to their spouses and children. Visit www.gibill.va.gov for details.

- Several states have adopted The Interstate Compact for Educational Opportunity for Military Children, which creates uniform standards for students transferring from other schools. Check to see if your state qualifies when moving your family.

- Military spouses have other education options, as well:

  - The National Military Family Association sponsors the Joanne Holbrook Patton Military Spouse Scholarship Program, which provides educational funds for spouses.

  - The Folds of Honor Foundation provides generous scholarships for spouses of servicemembers disabled or killed in the line of duty during the Global War on Terror.

So What?

There are literally hundreds of schools that accept G.I. Bill funds, and yet a staggering number of military members fail to take advantage of this program. This should be one of your first considerations when looking at schools.

Some states extend in-state tuition benefits to dependents of servicemembers. The DoD has an In-State Tuition Map that lists participating schools.

Review of Last Lesson

1. What does diversification mean, and how does it affect your risk in investing?

2. Are mutual funds for long-term or short-term investing?

3. Explain Dave's four-fold diversification strategy for long-term investing.

Small Group Discussion and Accountability

1. What do you think when you see retirement-aged people working in grocery stores? Is that what you want to do when you retire?

2. What motivates you to get serious about your retirement plan?

3. Should you ever *temporarily* stop adding to your retirement plan? If so, why? When should you start up again?

4. Do you believe it is possible to be wealthy at retirement by simply making wise decisions with your current pay? Explain.

5. Does college funding come before or after retirement savings according to the Baby Steps? Why?

6. Would you feel guilty taking care of your own retirement plan before putting money aside for your child's college education?

7. How does living by a monthly budget help you prepare for retirement?

8. Have you ever taken advantage of the G.I. Bill? Was it a good experience? Explain.

Homework

1. **Complete the Monthly Retirement Planning form** in the forms section of this workbook to determine how much money you should be saving every month for retirement.

2. **Complete the Monthly College Planning form** in the forms section of this workbook if you have children who will be heading to college.

online resources

daveramsey.com/mil-tools

Take advantage of your online toolkit!
Download PDF and audio files of this week's lesson for review at anytime.

You can also download all of the budget forms to keep you on track.

Bonus Lessons:
Go online to enjoy extra lessons that are only available in your online toolkit.

FROM FRUITION TO TUITION

ANSWER KEY

Wealth	$700,000
15%	Out
Favored	Pocket
Qualified	Borrow
Plan	60%
Earned	20%
$5,000	20%
Investment	Match
After	Roth
Free	401(k)
Save	College
Choices	IRA
Bracket	529
Invested	You
Flexibility	Freezes
Self	Age
15%	UTMA
Pension	UGMA
Roth	Not
Contract	Transfer
Matches	Listed
Always	Custodian
Leave	Insurance
Direct	Savings
Transfer	Pre-paid

Real Estate and Mortgages

Keeping the American Dream from Becoming a Nightmare

Baby Step 6 ™

Pay off your home _____.

Selling a Home

When selling a home, you should think like a _____.

The home should be in "near perfect" condition.

The return on investment of fix-up dollars is _____.

The most important aspect of preparation is attention to the _____ appeal.

When selling your home, make sure that it is listed on the _____.

When selling, statistical research has found that the best realtors are worth _____ than they cost.

The exposure through the _____ Listing Service is worth it.

When selecting a realtor, do not rely on _____ or _____.

These are professionals. You should always _____ them.

Offering a home _____ will typically not make a sale. If the buyer asks for a warranty, then consider it with that offer.

Buying a Home

Home ownership is a great investment for three main reasons:

1. It's a _____ savings plan.

2. It's an _____ hedge.

3. It grows virtually _____ - _____.

   You can have a gain of $250,000 single or $500,000 married and pay zero tax on the sale of your personal residence if you hold it at least two years.

Title insurance insures you against an _____ title, which is when your proper ownership is in question. It is a good buy.

Always get a land _____ if buying more than a standard subdivision lot.

Realtors' access to the _____ system can make house hunting easier, but be careful. Many agents can only think like retailers, which is not what you want when buying.

"Prepare your outside work, make it fit for yourself in the field; and afterward build your house."

– Proverbs 24:27 (NKJV)

NOTES

What To Buy

Buy in the _____ price range of the neighborhood.

Homes appreciate in good neighborhoods and are priced based on three things: _____, _____, and _____!

If possible, buy near _____ or with a _____.

Buy bargains by _____ bad landscaping, outdated carpet, ugly wallpaper, and the Elvis print in the master bedroom.

However...

Always buy a home that is (or can be) attractive from the _____ and has a good basic _____.

Have the home inspected mechanically and structurally by a certified _____ _____.

Appraisals are an "_____ of value," but it's a better opinion than the current homeowner has. Always order one if in doubt.

What Not To Buy

1. _____ or _____ _____

2. _____

Mortgages

First, remember to _____ debt.

The best mortgage is the _____% down plan.

But if you must take a mortgage...

Do not buy until you are ready. That means you are out of debt with a fully funded emergency fund.

There is nothing wrong with _____ for a little while. This demonstrates _____ and wisdom.

Get a payment of no more than _____% of your take home pay on a _____ fixed-rate loan, with at least _____% down. Have a fully funded emergency fund left over after closing.

Why choose a 15-year mortgage?

(Figures based on 6% APR)

I. $225,000	15 years	Pay	$1,899 /mo
II. $225,000	30 years	Pay	$1,349 /mo
		Difference	$550 /mo

But after 10 years...

The 15-year loan has a balance of $98,210 while the 30-year loan has a balance of $188,292!

During that 10 years, you would have paid almost $162,000 on the 30-year mortgage, but only paid down the loan by $36,708!

NOTES

123

Horrible Mortgage Options

To calculate how an ARM adjusts, see "How to Figure the Change in Your ARM" at the end of this lesson.

1. Adjustable Rate Mortgages (ARMs) were brought on with the advent of _____ interest rates in the early 1980's.

   • The concept of the ARM is to _____ the risk of higher interest rates to the _____ and, in return, the lender gives a lower rate up front.

   • Of course, _____ _____ loans are a bad idea because you are only paying the interest—*duh!*

   • You can qualify for more home with ARMs, but the risk of financial stress later is not worth it.

The FTC says that reverse mortgage options have the most fraud in the mortgage business.

2. _____ Mortgages

   • Bad idea because you are putting a paid-for home at risk and the fees are horrible.

3. _____, or Bi-Weekly Payoff

   • Allows you to make a half-payment every two weeks, which equals 13 payments a year. The reason it pays off early is because you make one extra payment a year.

   • Do not pay a fee for this option. You can easily do this on your own.

4. _____ Advantages of a Mortgage

- Do not fall for the myth that you should keep your mortgage for the tax advantages. The math doesn't work.

Where's the Tax Advantage?

Mortgage Amount	Interest Rate	Annual Interest Paid
$200,000	**5%**	**$10,000**

Mortgage interest is tax-deductible, so you would not have to pay taxes on this $10,000. That is why many people tell you to keep the mortgage. But what does this really save you?

Taxable Amount	Tax Bracket	Annual Taxes Paid
$10,000	**25%**	**$2,500**

So, if you keep your mortgage just for the "tax advantages," all you are really doing is sending $10,000 to the bank instead of sending $2,500 to the IRS. Where's the *"advantage"* in that?

Basic Ways to Finance a Home

1. _____, usually through FNMA and privately insured against default.

- Down payments range from 5% to 20% or more.

- These loans are available in all forms and formats.

- PMI is _____ mortgage insurance.

You can avoid PMI with a 20% down payment or by paying your existing mortgage down to 20% loan-to-value.

_____ **NOTES**

_____

_____

_____

_____

The VA loan was established to help the veteran purchase a home—certainly a good goal. However, the added fees and higher interest rate usually make VA loans more expensive than conventional mortgages. Plus, the zero-down option often leads many vets to buy more house than they can actually afford in the long run.

2. _____, which is insured by HUD—the federal government.

- Down payments are as low as _____% and are used on lower-priced homes.

- These loans are currently _____ expensive than conventional financing and should be avoided.

3. _____, which is insured by the Veterans Administration.

- Designed to benefit the veteran; the seller pays everything, allowing a true zero-down purchase.

- With a good down payment, the conventional loan is a _____ deal.

4. _____ financing is when you pay the owner over time, making him/her the mortgage holder.

- This is a _____ way to finance because you can be creative in the structure of the loan.

   Example: No payments for a year, interest rates that graduate, or discount for early payoff.

How To Figure Your New Payment

Monthly Payment per $1,000 in Loan Amount

Use this worksheet to estimate the monthly mortgage payment on a 15-year loan compared to a 30-year loan.

Rate	15-Year	30-Year
4.5%	7.65	5.07
5.0%	7.91	5.37
5.5%	8.17	5.68
6.0%	8.44	6.00
6.5%	8.71	6.32
7.0%	8.99	6.66
7.5%	9.28	7.00
8.0%	9.56	7.34
8.5%	9.85	7.69
9.0%	10.15	8.05
9.5%	10.44	8.41
10.0%	10.75	8.78
10.5%	11.05	9.15
11.0%	11.37	9.52
11.5%	11.68	9.90
12.0%	12.00	10.29

_____ / 1,000 = _____ X _____ = _____

Sales Price / 1,000 = #1000's X Factor = Monthly Payment

Example: Sales Price - $150,000, 15 years at 6%

$150,000 / 1,000 = 150 X 8.44 = $1,266

Sales Price / 1,000 = #1000's X Factor = Monthly Payment

NOTES

This worksheet helps you decide whether or not it would make sense to refinance your current mortgage to a lower-interest loan.

Should I Refinance?

Current principal and interest payment (not including taxes & insurance)   _____

New principal and interest payment   –   _____

Equals monthly savings   =   _____

_____   /   _____   =   _____

Total closing costs divided by savings   =   Number of months to break even

Example: Refinance on a $150,000 Mortgage at 8% to 6.5%

$1,434 current payment - $1,307 new payment = $127 savings

$2,300 closing cost divided by $127 savings = 18 months

Will you stay in your home longer than the number of months to break even? If so, you are a candidate for a refinance.

ESTIMATED CLOSING COSTS TABLE

Loan Amount	Closing Costs	Loan Amount	Closing Costs
30,000	1,500	75,000	1,850
35,000	1,550	80,000	1,900
40,000	1,600	85,000	1,925
45,000	1,650	90,000	1,950
50,000	1,700	95,000	1,975
55,000	1,725	100,000	2,000
60,000	1,775	150,000	2,300
65,000	1,800	200,000	2,600
70,000	1,825	250,000	2,900

How to Figure the Change in Your ARM

Your Adjustable Rate Mortgage (ARM) adjusts based on the movement of an index. You can find your index in your original note or mortgage. The most commonly used index is the Treasury Bill (T-Bill). The one-year ARM uses the one-year T-Bill, the three-year ARM uses the three-year T-Bill, and so on. Other commonly used indexes are the LIBOR and the 11th District Cost of Funds.

First, find out what index you use and when it is adjusted.

Next, find out (also from your loan paperwork) what margin was assigned to your loan (usually 2.59).

Basically, your ARM adjusts as the index moves.

The index is usually published daily in *The Wall Street Journal*.

So, if you have a one-year ARM that adjusts with the one-year T-Bill and a margin of 2.59 (which is typical), then, at the one-year anniversary of your closing, you would look up the one-year T-Bill in *The Wall Street Journal*. Add the T-Bill to your margin and you have your new rate (if it is not capped).

Example: T-Bill 4.41 plus margin 2.59 = 7% new interest rate.

Warning: Almost all ARMs start below margin the first year, guaranteeing a payment increase at anniversary unless rates DROP.

Listen Up!
Special Insights for Military Families

- Military families should be aware that several provisions within The Housing and Economic Recovery Act of 2008 (HR 3221) apply uniquely to them.

  - Military housing allowances are excluded from counting as income when qualifying for low-income housing.

  - Veterans' benefits received as a lump sum can be treated as monthly benefits when qualifying for Section 8 Housing.

- The military will help cover moving expenses, and the amount is determined by destination, rank, and whether or not you have dependents. Overall, however, it is wise not to collect a houseful of large furniture while on active duty. Strive to travel light for easier moves throughout your military career.

So What?

Active-duty servicemembers should plan for a PCS move about every three years. A moving plan is vital, especially since you will most likely not know whether on-base housing is available until you arrive, and because on-base housing often has a long waiting list.

Servicemembers who choose to live in off-base housing receive a Basic Allowance for Housing (BAH). The amount of BAH is determined by your rank and whether or not you have dependents. BAH is designed to cover the **average** cost of housing in the local area, so it may or may not cover **all** of your housing expenses.

Buying a home for each relocation is generally not the best approach. Slow down, follow the guidelines in this lesson, and make sure that your home will be a blessing—every time.

Review of Last Lesson

1. What are some specific ways in which your unique personality style impacts your work life?

2. Discuss the three-year professional plan you outlined for yourself in the last lesson.

Small Group Discussion and Accountability

1. What does it mean to be "house poor"? Is anyone here in that situation?

2. Is it ever okay to rent for a while? Why or why not?

3. Have you ever been late on a mortgage payment? If so, how did that make you feel?

4. What are the dangers in 30-year mortgages, adjustable rate loans, and home equity loans?

5. If you have to take out a mortgage, what guidelines does Dave recommend? According to those principles, how much house can you actually afford?

6. How would paying off your home early make you feel? How would it affect your retirement?

7. Why does Dave suggest servicemembers avoid VA loans?

8. Would you ever choose to be a long-distance landlord? Why do many servicemembers unexpectedly find themselves in this type of situation?

Homework

If you have not done it yet, check out the bonus lessons in your online toolkit. Go to daveramsey.com/mil-tools.

online resources
™

daveramsey.com/mil-tools

Take advantage of your online toolkit!
Download PDF and audio files of this week's lesson for review at anytime.

You can also download all of the budget forms to keep you on track.

Bonus Lessons:
Go online to enjoy extra lessons that are only available in your online toolkit.

REAL ESTATE AND MORTGAGES

ANSWER KEY

Early	Opinion
Retailer	Trailers
Enormous	Mobile
Curb	Homes
Internet	Timeshares
More	Hate
Multiple	100%
Friendships	Renting
Relatives	Patience
Interview	25%
Warranty	15-year
Forced	10%
Inflation	High
Tax	Transfer
Free	Borrower
Unclean	Interest
Survey	Only
MLS	Reverse
Bottom	Accelerated
Location	Tax
Location	Conventional
Location	Private
Water	FHA
View	3%
Overlooking	More
Street	VA
Floorplan	Better
Home	Owner
Inspector	Great

Dave Ramsey's
Financial Peace
MILITARY EDITION

That's Not Good Enough!™

How To Buy Only Big, Big Bargains

BONUS LESSON: VIDEO AVAILABLE IN YOUR ONLINE TOOLKIT

Ground Rules For Big Bargains

It is proper to get a great deal if you:

1. Have in no way _____ the truth.

2. Have not set out to _____ the other party.

3. Have created a _____ - _____ deal.

The First Key

The first key to opening the door to huge bargains is learning to _____ everything.

Win-win deals really work, so don't be _____ to _____ for the deal!

Lucky Seven Basic Rules of Negotiating

1. Always tell the absolute _____.

2. Use the power of _____.

   • Cash is _____.

   • Cash is _____.

   • Cash has _____.

3. Understand and use "_____ _____ power."

4. _____ _____.

5. "That's not _____ _____."

6. _____ guy, _____ guy.

7. The "If I" _____ _____ technique.

_____ NOTES

_____

_____

_____

_____

The Second Key

- The second key to opening the door to huge bargains is that you must have _____.

- Don't get _____ to a purchase.

The Third Key

- The third key to opening the door to huge bargains is that you must know _____ to _____ deals.

- _____ something of value, goods, or just your _____.

Places to Find Great Deals

1. _____
2. Estate Sales
3. _____ _____
4. Couponing
5. _____ _____
6. Repo Lot
7. _____ _____
8. Refunding
9. _____
10. Pawn Shops
11. _____ _____
12. Classified Ads
13. _____ _____
14. Conventions

Love, Mom

During a period of economic hardship due to high interest rates in the real estate business, my mother sent me the following poem in the mail.

THE ROOSTER AND THE HEN

Said the Little Red Rooster, "Believe me things are tough!
Seems the worms are getting scarcer and I cannot find enough.
What's become of all those fat ones? It's a mystery to me.
There were thousands through that rainy spell,
But now, where can they be?"

But the Old Black Hen who heard him didn't grumble or complain,
She had lived through lots of dry spells;
She had lived through floods of rain.
She picked a new and undug spot, The ground was hard and firm,
"I must go to the worms," she said. "The worms won't come to me."

The Rooster vainly spent his day,
Through habit, by the ways
Where fat round worms had passed in squads back in the rainy days.
When nightfall found him supperless, he growled in accents rough,
"I'm hungry as a fowl can be, conditions sure are tough."

But the Old Black Hen hopped to her perch
And dropped her eyes to sleep
And murmured in a drowsy tone, "Young man, hear this and weep.
I'm full of worms and happy
For I've eaten like a pig.
The worms were there as always
But, boy I had to dig!"

This was a Depression Era Poem. Strange it still applies today.
Love,
Mom

Listen Up!
Special Insights for Military Families

- Rising inflation rates are endangering servicemembers' purchasing power. Therefore, it is crucial to make well-informed, budget-concious buying decisions—*every time!*

- Servicemembers have access to commissaries located in the United States and sometimes those in foreign countries. Retired servicemembers, National Guard members, and Reservists (active, inactive, or retired) also have domestic commissary access.

- Check with your individual Service's Financial Readiness organization to find out what helpful tips, tools, and pamphlets are available to you. For example, one Army pamphlet offers a great deal of helpful advice in the area of purchasing and personal finance, such as:

  - **It is your money.** You can spend it unwisely, or you can use it to buy things that will make your life happier, more comfortable, and more enjoyable. Plan your spending.

  - **Sign your name with care.** You may not believe you have much to protect, but you can give away your future with the stroke of a pen.

So What?

It is more important than ever to make your dollar go farther. You do this with a budget, careful buying decisions, and effective bargaining techniques. Don't settle for what the sticker says; instead, be bold enough to look the salesperson in the eye and say, "That's not good enough!"

Also, when buying something, be sure to ask if the store has a military discount. Many stores offer this as a service to men and women in uniform. Never be ashamed to ask; after all, if a store has this discount in place, it is because they want to honor and thank you!

Review of Last Lesson

1. The purpose of insurance is to:

    A. Lower risk   B. Transfer risk   C. Eliminate risk

2. True or False: Insurance is an essential planning tool. Why or why not?

3. At what point in the Baby Steps should insurance be included in your financial plan?

4. Hold up your monthly zero-based budget.

    A. Discuss how much easier or harder it was to do this time compared to the first one. Be *honest* with each other.

    B. Discuss what you have learned about handling money.

Small Group Discussion and Accountability

1. Why do most people avoid negotiating for deals?

2. Describe a time when you found a great bargain. Was it a win-win?

3. Why is integrity so important in the area of bargain hunting?

4. How often do you actually ask for a deal when shopping?

5. When you are at the store and the cashier gives you too much money back, what do you do?

    A. Keep it and don't say anything.   B. Return it immediately.

6. Are you still plagued by impulse purchases? What goes through your heart and mind when you are tempted to spend?

7. How is your envelope system coming along? Are you sticking to your written budget?

8. Will shopping at the Commissary/BX always save you money?

9. Have you ever asked for a "military discount" when purchasing?

Homework

1. **Tell a friend about FPM.** If *Financial Peace Military Edition* is making a difference in your life, share the good news with someone!

2. **Try at least one of these buying techniques this week** and report back on your experience in the next class session.

THAT'S NOT GOOD ENOUGH!

Misrepresented	Away
Harm	Patience
Win-Win	Married
Negotiate	Where
Afraid	Find
Ask	Trade
Truth	Services
Cash	Individuals
Emotional	Public
Visual	Auctions
Immediacy	Garage
Walk	Sales
Away	Flea
Shut Up	Markets
Good	Foreclosures
Enough	Online
Good	Auctions
Bad	Consignment
Take	Sales

Dave Ramsey's
Financial Peace
MILITARY EDITION

Working In Your Strengths™
Careers and Extra Jobs

BONUS LESSON: VIDEO AVAILABLE IN YOUR ONLINE TOOLKIT

Change Happens

The average job is now only _____ years in length.

This means that the average worker could have as many as _____ different jobs in his or her working lifetime.

Small business is changing the way we think about work. _____% of the companies in America have fewer than 100 employees.

Discover Your Strengths and Weaknesses

How can you know _____ you ought to be and _____ you ought to be doing if you don't know _____ you are?

Speaker and author Marcus Buckingham has identified some common myths that often rob people of having fulfillment and enjoyment in their careers.

Myth: As you grow, you _____.

Truth: You do not _____ your personality.

Myth: You will learn and grow the most in the areas in which you are _____.

Truth: You grow in your _____. You will grow the most in the areas that you already know and love the most.

Identify Your Motivation and Passion

Career coach Dan Miller reminds us that _____ is ultimately never enough compensation for doing a job.

Find something that blends your skills, _____, personality traits, _____, dreams, and _____.

Understand Your Unique Personality

The _____ profile is a simple exercise that will yield tremendous insight into how you process decisions and what your natural tendencies may be.

- The D (_____) person is a hard-charging driver that is task-oriented and first looks to _____.

- The I (_____) person is people-oriented, fun, outgoing, and generally concerned about people-pleasing, so they first look to _____.

- The S (_____) person is amiable, loyal, does not like conflict, and is concerned about _____.

- The C (_____) person is analytical, loves detail, factual, can seem rigid, and loves _____.

"Life is never made unbearable by circumstances but only by lack of meaning and purpose."

– Viktor Frankl

"Until you make peace with who you are, you will never be content with what you have."

– Doris Mortman

"Know thyself, and to thine own self be true."

– Shakespeare

"The unexamined life is not worth living."

– Socrates

NOTES

DISC Personality Profile

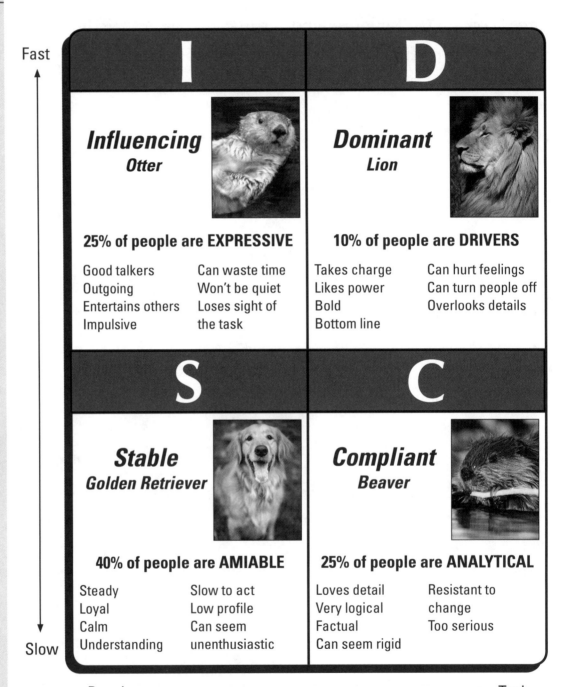

	Fast	
I		**D**

Influencing
Otter

25% of people are EXPRESSIVE

Good talkers	Can waste time
Outgoing	Won't be quiet
Entertains others	Loses sight of
Impulsive	the task

Dominant
Lion

10% of people are DRIVERS

Takes charge	Can hurt feelings
Likes power	Can turn people off
Bold	Overlooks details
Bottom line	

S

Stable
Golden Retriever

40% of people are AMIABLE

Steady	Slow to act
Loyal	Low profile
Calm	Can seem
Understanding	unenthusiastic

C

Compliant
Beaver

25% of people are ANALYTICAL

Loves detail	Resistant to
Very logical	change
Factual	Too serious
Can seem rigid	

Slow

People ←————————→ Task

Job Hunting

Companies do not start out looking for _____. They have a specific _____ and they need someone to meet it.

Develop a strategy:

- Identify your _____.

- _____ everything you can about them.

Résumés

When it is time to contact the company, think of it like starting a new _____ with a person.

After you target the companies where you would most like to work, you are going to contact them at least three times.

- Introduction _____

- Cover Letter and Résumé

- _____ Follow-up

Interviews and jobs come from persistent follow-up and _____.

"The major difference between successful and unsuccessful job hunters is not skill, education, or ability, but the way they go about their job hunt."

– Anonymous

"Genius is the ability to clearly visualize the objective."

– Anonymous

"The secret of success is focus of purpose."

– Thomas Edison

NOTES

Home-Based Business Ideas:

Accounting
Auditing
Bookkeeping
Columnist
Computer Technician
Copywriter
Customer Service
Data Entry Clerk
Editor
Fundraiser
Graphic Artist
Information Specialist
LAN Manager
Lawyer
Market Researcher
Online Auctions
Probation Officer
Programmer
Public Relations
Real Estate Agent
Records Manager
Reporter
Researcher
Sales Representative
Systems Analyst
Technical Writer
Telemarketer
Transcriber
Translator
Travel Agent
Web Design

Part-Time Job Ideas:

Car Detailing
Carpentry
Handyman
Maid Service
Newspaper Delivery
Pizza Delivery
Waiter
Yard Work

Interviews

Present yourself well. You are the _____, so make it the best one available.

Be on _____, address everyone by _____, offer a firm, confident _____, and maintain _____ contact at all times.

Designate a time to _____ _____ after the interview... and DO IT!

Overtime and Extra Jobs

Raising your income _____-term is a career track issue.
Raising it _____-term means the dreaded part-time job.

How do you get started with an extra job?

- Be willing to _____ to win.

- Have a detailed _____ so you can see the finish line. This gives you hope!

- Choose the _____ or start a _____ - _____ business.

- Don't _____ _____!

Beware! Do not allow your work to be the source of all your satisfaction and self-_____.

An American Creed

I Do Not Choose to Be a Common Man

It is my right to be uncommon—if I can.

I seek opportunity—not security. I do not wish to be a kept citizen, humbled and dulled by having the state look after me.

I want to take the calculated risk; to dream and to build, to fail and to succeed.

I refuse to barter incentive for a dole. I prefer the challenges of life to the guaranteed existence; the thrill of fulfillment to the stale calm of utopia.

I will not trade freedom for beneficence nor my dignity for a handout. I will never cower before any master nor bend to any threat.

It is my heritage to stand erect, proud and unafraid; to think and act for myself, enjoy the benefit of my creations and to face the world boldly and say, "This I have done."

By Dean Alfange

*Originally published in *This Week* Magazine.
Later reprinted in *The Reader's Digest*, October 1952 and January 1954.

The Honorable Dean Alfange was an American statesman born December 2, 1899, in Constantinople (now Istanbul). He was raised in upstate New York. He served in the U.S. Army during World War I and attended Hamilton College, graduating in the class of 1922. He attended Columbia University where he received his law degree and opened a practice in Manhattan. In 1942, Alfange was the American Labor Party candidate for governor of New York and a founder of the Liberal Party of New York. Dean Alfange was also Professor Emeritus at UMass Amherst and a leading figure in various pro-Zionist organizations. Between other actions, in November 1943, he appeared before the House of Representatives and addressed them on the rescue of the Jewish people of Europe. He died in Manhattan at the age of 91 on October 27, 1989.

"Think beyond your lifetime if you want to accomplish something truly worthwhile."

– Walt Disney

"Do not overwork to be rich; because of your own understanding, cease! Will you set your eyes on that which is not? For riches certainly make themselves wings; they fly away like an eagle toward heaven."

– Proverbs 23:4-5 (NKJV)

NOTES

Listen Up!
Special Insights for Military Families

- The military often provides highly specialized training, education, and certification. Always list these things on your résumé when job hunting.

- USERRA protects servicemembers from losing their jobs due to an extended deployment. Under the USERRA, Reservists and Guard members are entitled to return to their jobs and continue participating in an employer's retirement plan while on active duty.

- Military service, especially in wartime, can create levels of emotional stress that civilians cannot imagine. As you one day re-enter the public sector, you may want to take advantage of the DoD's provisions for safeguarding emotional health.

  - The DoD has entered into an agreement with the U.S. Public Health Service (PHS) to increase mental health services available to active duty servicemembers and retirees, as well as their families.

  - The DoD also offers a video depicting how servicemembers and families may be affected by combat and deployment issues. Examples include post-traumatic stress disorder, alcohol abuse, nightmares, and emotional distress.

  - The DoD's Mental Health Self-Assessment Program offers servicemembers and their families anonymous mental health and alcohol self-assessments online (militarymentalhealth.org).

So What?

Most servicemembers have the prospect of a second career looming in their future. That's why it is so important for you to take care of yourself—physically, mentally, emotionally, and spiritually.

Review of Last Lesson

1. What is an IRA?

2. Should you ever cash in or borrow against pre-taxed retirement savings early to pay off debt? Why or why not?

3. Is the G.I. Bill a good deal? New legislation allows you to transfer it to your spouse and/or dependents. Does that make it more valuable to servicemembers?

Small Group Discussion and Accountability

1. If you could do anything you wanted and money was no object, what would you do? How is your current work preparing you to do that?

2. What areas of growth or education will help you along your career path?

3. Based on your unique personality, what strengths do you bring to your particular organization or the workplace in general?

4. Talk about the danger of being a workaholic. How can it affect your life, spirit, and family? Is this a non-issue if you are single? How can you better balance your military responsibilities with your family responsibilities?

5. If you are allowed to work off-duty, what could you do to earn extra money? How could this gazelle intensity affect your debt snowball or other short-term goals?

6. Have you stopped using credit cards for purchases?

Homework

1. **Review the DISC chart in your workbook** to determine if your current line of work naturally fits within your unique personality style.

2. **Lay out a three-year professional plan** in which you envision exactly what you want to be doing three years from now. Include your military plans, including reenlistment, promotions, retirement, etc.

online resources ™

Take advantage of your online toolkit!
Download PDF and audio files of this week's lesson for review at anytime.

You can also download all of the budget forms to keep you on track.

Bonus Lessons:
Go online to enjoy extra lessons that are only available in your online toolkit.

daveramsey.com/mil-tools

WORKING IN YOUR STRENGTHS

2.1	Need
20	Target
98.3%	Learn
Where	Relationship
What	Letter
Who	Phone
Change	Networking
Outgrow	Product
Weakest	Time
Strengths	Name
Money	Handshake
Abilities	Eye
Values	Follow
Passions	Up
DISC	Long
Dominant	Short
Problems	Sacrifice
Influencing	Plan
People	Job
Stable	Home
Pace	Based
Compliant	Give
Procedure	Up
You	Worth

Of Mice and Mutual Funds™

Understanding Investments

BONUS LESSON: VIDEO AVAILABLE IN YOUR ONLINE TOOLKIT

KISS Rule of Investing

- Keep it _____, _____!

- It does not mean that you are stupid if you make _____ investments.

- Never invest purely for _____ _____.

- Never invest using _____ money.

Diversification

- Diversification means to _____ _____.

- Diversification _____ risk.

The Power of Diversification

Investor 1
- Invest $10,000 for 25 years at 7% (compounded annually)

Investor 2
- Invest $2,000 and lose it all
- Invest $2,000 under your mattress
- Invest $2,000 at 5% return
- Invest $2,000 at 10% return
- Invest $2,000 at 15% return

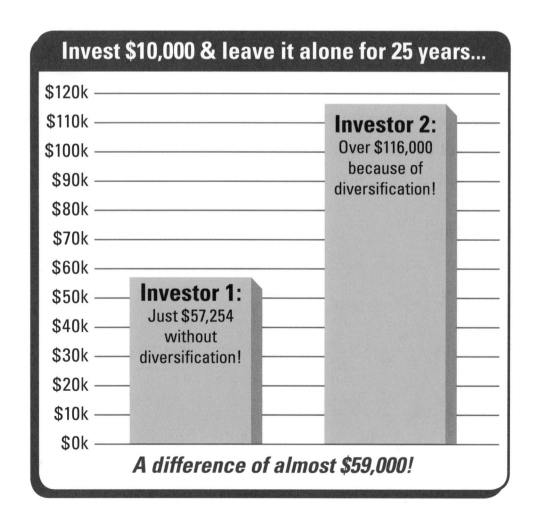

Invest $10,000 & leave it alone for 25 years...

Investor 1: Just $57,254 without diversification!

Investor 2: Over $116,000 because of diversification!

A difference of almost $59,000!

NOTES

Risk Return Ratio and Liquidity

- With virtually all investments, as the _____ goes up, so does the potential _____.

- When discussing investments, liquidity is _____.

- As there is more liquidity, there is typically _____ return.

Types of Investments

1. Money Markets

- A C.D. is a certificate of _____, typically at a bank.

- Money market mutual funds are _____ risk money market accounts with check-writing privileges. These are great for emergency funds.

2. Single Stocks

- Single stock investing carries an extremely _____ degree of risk.

- When you buy stock, you are buying a small piece of _____ in the company.

- Your return comes as the company increases in _____ or pays you, its owner, some of the profits (called _____).

3. Bonds

- A bond is a _____ instrument by which the company owes _____ money.

- Your return is the fluctuation in price and the _____ rate paid. _____ individuals do well with single bond purchases.

4. Mutual Funds

- Investors pool their _____ to invest.

- Professional portfolio managers manage the pool or _____.

- Your _____ comes as the _____ of the fund is increased.

- Mutual funds are good _____ term investments.

"An investment in knowledge always pays the best interest."

– Ben Franklin

"I'm putting all my money in taxes. It's the only thing guaranteed to go up."

– Mark Twain

Conservative Diversification:

25% – Balanced
25% – Growth
25% – Growth & Income
25% – International

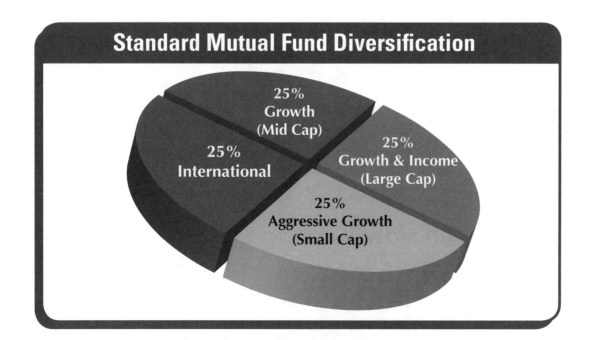

Standard Mutual Fund Diversification

25% Growth (Mid Cap)
25% Growth & Income (Large Cap)
25% International
25% Aggressive Growth (Small Cap)

NOTES

5. Rental Real Estate

- Least _____ consumer investment.

- You should have a lot of _____ before using real estate as an investment.

6. Annuities

- Annuities are _____ accounts with an insurance company.

- _____ annuities are at a low interest rate of around 5%, aren't *really* fixed, and are a bad long-term investment.

- _____ annuities are mutual funds sheltered by the annuity covering, thereby allowing the mutual fund to grow tax-deferred.

7. Horrible Investments

- Gold
- Commodities and Futures
- Day Trading
- Viaticals

Conclusion

If you do not understand an investment well enough to teach someone else how it works, DON'T BUY IT!

Build wealth slowly.

Monthly Debt Payments Rob You Of Your Retirement!

Years Invested Monthly At 12% Per Year

Monthly Payments	5 years	10 years	15 years	25 years	40 years
$100	8,167	23,004	49,958	187,885	1,176,477
$200	16,334	46,008	99,916	375,769	2,352,954
$300	24,500	69,012	149,874	563,654	3,529,431
$400	32,668	92,015	199,832	751,538	4,705,909
$500	40,835	115,019	249,790	939,423	5,882,386
$600	49,002	138,023	299,748	1,127,308	7,058,863
$700	57,168	161,027	349,706	1,315,193	8,235,341
$800	65,336	184,031	399,664	1,503,077	9,411,818
$900	73,503	207,034	449,622	1,690,962	10,588,295
$1,000	81,669	230,039	499,580	1,878,847	11,764,772
$1,200	98,004	276,046	599,496	2,254,616	14,117,727
$1,500	122,504	345,058	749,370	2,818,270	17,647,159
$2,000	163,339	460,077	999,160	3,757,693	23,529,545

However, retirement can look pretty sweet if you don't have any debt.

Listen Up!
Special Insights for Military Families

- Servicemembers and other government workers are eligible for the Thrift Savings Plan (TSP). This is a strong retirement plan that servicemembers should take advantage of.

  - We recommend investing 60% in the C Fund, 20% in the S Fund, and 20% in the I Fund. This will be covered in greater detail in the following lesson and in the optional military bonus lesson.

  - We do not recommend the F, G, or L Funds at all.

- Servicemembers should always roll their TSP funds into an IRA when they leave the military.

- Guard members and Reservists have special retirement provisions under the Uniformed Services Employment and Reemployment Rights Act (USERRA):

  - You can continue contributing to your employer-sponsored retirement plan and still receive any matching funds.

  - You have up to five years to catch up on retirement contributions missed due to active service.

  - If your retirement plan includes a company match, your employer must match your catch-up contributions.

  - If your employer contributes to a pension plan, they must continue contributing during your deployment.

So What?

Investing may seem intimidating at first, but the concepts are relatively simple to understand. Keep in mind that investing calls for a long-term mindset. It is all about delaying pleasure so that you have more to enjoy.

Review of Last Lesson

1. What are the seven basic rules of negotiating?

2. Did the previous lesson change any of your shopping habits this week?

Small Group Discussion and Accountability

1. Explain what a mutual fund is and how it works.

2. Why is it dangerous to invest with borrowed money?

3. Why is diversification important?

4. Why are single stocks so dangerous?

5. Why does Dave stress the importance of becoming debt free (except the mortgage) before you begin your long-term investing?

6. Why is it so important to make your own educated, well-informed decisions, rather than simply surrendering your decisions to an advisor?

7. Talk about how important it is for spouses to be on the same page when it comes to dumping debt and investing.

8. Do you currently participate in the Thrift Savings Plan? Why or why not?

9. If you are eligible for the Savings Deposit Program, have you taken advantage of it?

Homework

Calculate how much your debt payments are robbing from your retirement. Use the chart on page 157.

online resources ™

daveramsey.com/mil-tools

Take advantage of your online toolkit!
Download PDF and audio files of this week's lesson for review at anytime.

You can also download all of the budget forms to keep you on track.

Bonus Lessons:
Go online to enjoy extra lessons that are only available in your online toolkit.

OF MICE AND MUTUAL FUNDS

Simple

Stupid

Simple

Tax

Savings

Borrowed

Spread

Around

Lowers

Risk

Return

Availability

Less

Deposit

Low

High

Ownership

Value

Dividends

Debt

You

Interest

Few

Money

Fund

Return

Value

Long

Liquid

Cash

Savings

Fixed

Variable

Financial Forms

The Basic Quickie Budget (Instructions)

This form will help you get your feet wet in the area of budgeting. It is only one page and should not be intimidating as you get started. The purpose of this form is to show you exactly how much money you need every month in order to survive. We won't get into the details of your credit card bills, student loans, and other consumer debts here. *This is just to give you a starting point as you begin to take control of your money.* You will learn how to create a full monthly cash flow plan in the third class session.

There are four columns on this form:

1. Monthly Total

- This column shows you how much you are spending on necessities each month.

- If you do not know the amount, write down your best estimate.

- If an estimate is grossly inaccurate, then you may have never even noticed how much you were spending in that area before now. Don't beat yourself up about this!

2. Payoff Total

- Write down how much money is required to completely pay off that item.

- This line only appears in the relevant categories (mortgage, car debt, etc.)

3. How Far Behind?

- If your account is past due in any category, write down how many days you are behind.

- If you are up-to-date, simply write a zero or N/A (not applicable) here.

4. Type of Account

- Write in how this area is paid—by check, automatic bank draft, cash, etc.

- Early in the FPM course, you will see the benefits of using cash for certain items. Challenge yourself by identifying categories for which you can use cash only.

- The asterisks (*) on the form indicate areas in which a cash-based approach could be helpful.

The Basic Quickie Budget

Item	Monthly Total	Payoff Total	How Far Behind	Type of Account
GIVING	_____		_____	_____
SAVING	_____		_____	_____
HOUSING				
First Mortgage	_____	_____	_____	_____
Second Mortgage	_____	_____	_____	_____
Repairs/Mn. Fee	_____		_____	_____
UTILITIES				
Electricity	_____		_____	_____
Water	_____		_____	_____
Gas	_____		_____	_____
Phone	_____		_____	_____
Trash	_____		_____	_____
Cable	_____		_____	_____
*Food	_____		_____	_____
TRANSPORTATION				
Car Payment	_____	_____	_____	_____
Car Payment	_____	_____	_____	_____
*Gas & Oil	_____		_____	_____
*Repairs & Tires	_____		_____	_____
Car Insurance	_____		_____	_____
*CLOTHING	_____		_____	_____
PERSONAL				
Disability Ins.	_____		_____	_____
Health Insurance	_____		_____	_____
Life Insurance	_____		_____	_____
Child Care	_____		_____	_____
*Entertainment	_____		_____	_____
OTHER MISC.	_____		_____	_____

TOTAL MONTHLY NECESSITIES _____

Dave Ramsey's
Financial Peace
MILITARY EDITION

Major Components of a Healthy Financial Plan (Form 1)

	Action Needed	Action Date
Written Cash Flow Plan	_____	_____
Will and/or Estate Plan	_____	_____
Debt Reduction Plan	_____	_____
Tax Reduction Plan	_____	_____
Emergency Funding	_____	_____
Retirement Funding	_____	_____
College Funding	_____	_____
Charitable Giving	_____	_____
Teach My Children	_____	_____
Life Insurance	_____	_____
Health Insurance	_____	_____
Disability Insurance	_____	_____
Auto Insurance	_____	_____
Homeowner's Insurance	_____	_____

I (We) _____, (a) responsible adult(s), do hereby promise to take the above stated actions by the above stated dates to financially secure the well-being of my (our) family and myself (ourselves).

Signed:_____ Date:_____

Signed:_____ Date:_____

Dave Ramsey's
Financial Peace
MILITARY EDITION

Consumer Equity Sheet (Form 2)

ITEM / DESCRIBE	VALUE	–	DEBT	=	EQUITY
Real Estate _____	_____		_____		_____
Real Estate _____	_____		_____		_____
Car _____	_____		_____		_____
Car _____	_____		_____		_____
Cash On Hand	_____		_____		_____
Checking Account	_____		_____		_____
Checking Account	_____		_____		_____
Savings Account	_____		_____		_____
Savings Account	_____		_____		_____
Money Market Account	_____		_____		_____
Mutual Funds	_____		_____		_____
Retirement Plan	_____		_____		_____
Cash Value (Insurance)	_____		_____		_____
Household Items	_____		_____		_____
Jewelry	_____		_____		_____
Antiques	_____		_____		_____
Boat	_____		_____		_____
Unsecured Debt (Neg)	_____		_____		_____
Credit Card Debt (Neg)	_____		_____		_____
Other _____	_____		_____		_____
Other _____	_____		_____		_____
Other _____	_____		_____		_____
TOTAL	_____		_____		_____

Income Sources (Form 3)

SOURCE	AMOUNT	PERIOD/DESCRIBE
Salary 1	_____	_____
Salary 2	_____	_____
Salary 3	_____	_____
Bonus	_____	_____
Self-Employment	_____	_____
Interest Income	_____	_____
Dividend Income	_____	_____
Royalty Income	_____	_____
Rents	_____	_____
Notes	_____	_____
Alimony	_____	_____
Child Support	_____	_____
AFDC	_____	_____
Unemployment	_____	_____
Social Security	_____	_____
Pension	_____	_____
Annuity	_____	_____
Disability Income	_____	_____
Cash Gifts	_____	_____
Trust Fund	_____	_____
Other_____	_____	_____
Other_____	_____	_____
Other_____	_____	_____
TOTAL	_____	

Lump Sum Payment Planning (Form 4)

Payments you make on a non-monthly basis, such as insurance premiums and taxes, can be budget busters if you do not plan for them every month. Therefore, you must annualize the cost and convert these to monthly budget items. That way, you can save the money each month and will not be caught off-guard when your bi-monthly, quarterly, semi-annual, or annual bills come due. Simply divide the annual cost by 12 to determine the monthly amount you should save for each item.

ITEM NEEDED	ANNUAL AMOUNT		MONTHLY AMOUNT
Real Estate Taxes	_____	/ 12 =	_____
Homeowner's Insurance	_____	/ 12 =	_____
Home Repairs	_____	/ 12 =	_____
Replace Furniture	_____	/ 12 =	_____
Medical Bills	_____	/ 12 =	_____
Health Insurance	_____	/ 12 =	_____
Life Insurance	_____	/ 12 =	_____
Disability Insurance	_____	/ 12 =	_____
Car Insurance	_____	/ 12 =	_____
Car Repair/Tags	_____	/ 12 =	_____
Replace Car	_____	/ 12 =	_____
Clothing	_____	/ 12 =	_____
Tuition	_____	/ 12 =	_____
Bank Note	_____	/ 12 =	_____
IRS (Self-Employed)	_____	/ 12 =	_____
Vacation	_____	/ 12 =	_____
Gifts (including Christmas)	_____	/ 12 =	_____
Other _____	_____	/ 12 =	_____

Dave Ramsey's
Financial Peace
MILITARY EDITION

Monthly Cash Flow Plan (Instructions)

Every single dollar of your income should be allocated to some category on this form. When you're done, your total income minus expenses should equal zero. If it doesn't, then you need to adjust some categories (such as debt reduction, giving, or saving) so that it does equal zero. Use some common sense here, too. Do not leave things like clothes, car repairs, or home improvements off this list. If you don't plan for these things, then you're only setting yourself up for failure later.

Yes, this budget form is long. It's *really* long. We do that so that we can list practically every expense imaginable on this form to prevent you from forgetting something. Don't expect to put something on *every* line item. Just use the ones that are relevant to your specific situation.

Every main category on this form has subcategories. Fill in the monthly expense for each subcategory, and then write down the grand total for that category. Later, as you actually pay the bills and work through the month, use the Actually Spent column to record what you really spent in each area. If there is a substantial difference between what you budgeted and what you spent, then you'll need to readjust the budget to make up for the difference. If one category continually comes up over or short for two or three months, then you need to adjust the budgeted amount accordingly.

Use the % Take Home Pay column to record what percentage of your income actually goes to each category. Then, use the Recommended Percentages sheet (Form 6) to see if your percentages are in line with what we recommend.

Notes:

- An asterisk (*) beside an item indicates an area for which you should use the envelope system.

- The emergency fund should get all the savings until you've completed your full emergency fund of three to six months of expenses (Baby Step 3).

- Don't forget to include your annualized items from the Lump Sum Payment Planning sheet (Form 4), including your Christmas gift planning.

Monthly Cash Flow Plan (Form 5)

Budgeted Item	Sub Total	TOTAL	Actually Spent	% of Take Home Pay
CHARITABLE GIFTS		_____	_____	_____
SAVING				
Emergency Fund	_____		_____	
Retirement Fund	_____		_____	
College Fund	_____	_____	_____	_____
HOUSING				
First Mortgage	_____		_____	
Second Mortgage	_____		_____	
Real Estate Taxes	_____		_____	
Homeowner's Insurance	_____		_____	
Repairs or Maintenance Fee	_____		_____	
Replace Furniture	_____		_____	
Other _____	_____	_____	_____	_____
UTILITIES				
Electricity	_____		_____	
Water	_____		_____	
Gas	_____		_____	
Phone	_____		_____	
Trash	_____		_____	
Cable	_____	_____	_____	_____
*FOOD				
*Groceries	_____		_____	
*Restaurants	_____	_____	_____	_____
TRANSPORTATION				
Car Payment	_____		_____	
Car Payment	_____		_____	
*Gas and Oil	_____		_____	
*Repairs and Tires	_____		_____	
Car Insurance	_____		_____	
License and Taxes	_____		_____	
Car Replacement	_____	_____	_____	_____
PAGE 1 TOTAL			_____	_____

Monthly Cash Flow Plan (Form 5 – continued)

Budgeted Item	Sub Total	TOTAL	Actually Spent	% of Take Home Pay
*CLOTHING				
*Children	_____		_____	
*Adults	_____		_____	
*Cleaning/Laundry	_____	_____	_____	_____
MEDICAL/HEALTH				
Disability Insurance	_____		_____	
Health Insurance	_____		_____	
Doctor Bills	_____		_____	
Dentist	_____		_____	
Optometrist	_____		_____	
Medications	_____	_____	_____	_____
PERSONAL				
Life Insurance	_____		_____	
Child Care	_____		_____	
*Baby Sitter	_____		_____	
*Toiletries	_____		_____	
*Cosmetics	_____		_____	
*Hair Care	_____		_____	
Education/Adult	_____		_____	
School Tuition	_____		_____	
School Supplies	_____		_____	
Child Support	_____		_____	
Alimony	_____		_____	
Subscriptions	_____		_____	
Organization Dues	_____		_____	
Gifts (including Christmas)	_____		_____	
Miscellaneous	_____		_____	
*Pocket Money	_____	_____	_____	_____
PAGE 2 TOTAL		_____	_____	

Monthly Cash Flow Plan (Form 5 – continued)

Budgeted Item	Sub Total	TOTAL	Actually Spent	% of Take Home Pay
RECREATION				
*Entertainment	_____		_____	
Vacation	_____	_____	_____	_____
DEBTS (Hopefully -0-)				
Visa 1	_____		_____	
Visa 2	_____		_____	
Master Card 1	_____		_____	
Master Card 2	_____		_____	
American Express	_____		_____	
Discover Card	_____		_____	
Gas Card 1	_____		_____	
Gas Card 2	_____		_____	
Dept. Store Card 1	_____		_____	
Dept. Store Card 2	_____		_____	
Finance Co. 1	_____		_____	
Finance Co. 2	_____		_____	
Credit Line	_____		_____	
Student Loan 1	_____		_____	
Student Loan 2	_____		_____	
Other _____	_____		_____	
Other _____	_____		_____	
Other _____	_____		_____	
Other _____	_____		_____	
Other _____	_____	_____	_____	_____
PAGE 3 TOTAL		_____	_____	
PAGE 2 TOTAL		_____	_____	
PAGE 1 TOTAL		_____	_____	
GRAND TOTAL		_____	_____	

TOTAL HOUSEHOLD INCOME _____

ZERO

Dave Ramsey's
Financial Peace MILITARY EDITION

Recommended Percentages (Form 6)

How much of your income should be spent on housing, giving, food, etc.? Through experience and research, we recommend the following percentages. However, you should remember that these are only *recommended* percentages. If you have an unusually high or low income, then these numbers could change dramatically. For example, if you have a high income, the *percentage* that is spent on food will be much lower than someone who earns half of that.

If you find that you spend much more in one category than we recommend, however, it may be necessary to adjust your lifestyle in that area in order to enjoy more freedom and flexibility across the board.

ITEM	ACTUAL %	RECOMMENDED %
CHARITABLE GIFTS	_____	10 – 15%
SAVING	_____	5 – 10%
HOUSING	_____	25 – 35%
UTILITIES	_____	5 – 10%
FOOD	_____	5 – 15%
TRANSPORTATION	_____	10 – 15%
CLOTHING	_____	2 – 7%
MEDICAL/HEALTH	_____	5 – 10%
PERSONAL	_____	5 – 10%
RECREATION	_____	5 – 10%
DEBTS	_____	5 – 10%

Dave Ramsey's
Financial Peace
MILITARY EDITION

Allocated Spending Plan (Instructions)

Now that you've already planned out the entire month on the Monthly Cash Flow Plan (Form 5), let's get just a little bit more precise. On this form, you will allocate—or spend—all of your money from each individual pay period.

There are four columns on this form, representing the four weeks in a given month. You will use one column for each week you get paid. If you are married and your spouse earns an income, then you will both use this same form. For weeks in which you both receive a paycheck, simply add those two incomes together and use a single column. Be sure to write the pay date at the top of the column.

Now, go down the list and allocate each expense to a specific payday, using your bills' due dates as a guide. For example, if your phone bill is due on the 22nd and you get paid on the 15th and 30th, then you know that you would probably pay that bill from your income on the 15th. Some things, like utility bills, will be paid monthly, while other items, such as food and gasoline, could be weekly. The point here is to anticipate both your upcoming expenses and your upcoming income and plan accordingly.

Beside each line item, you'll see two blanks separated by a slash (/). Put the expense to the left of the slash and the remaining income from that pay period to the right of the slash. As you work your way down the column, the income remaining should diminish until you reach a perfect zero at the bottom of the list. If you have money left over at the end of the column, go back and adjust an area, such as savings or giving, so that you spend every single dollar.

This level of detail may be uncomfortable to you at first, but the payoff is worth it. By specifically naming every dollar before you actually get it in your hands, you will remove an incredible amount of stress and curb your overspending.

NOTES:

- If you have an irregular income, such as self-employment or commissions, you should use the Irregular Income Planning sheet (Form 8) instead of this Allocated Spending Plan.

- If you know that you have an impulse spending problem, then you may want to allocate more money to the Pocket Money category. That way, you are at least planning for it and setting up some boundaries for yourself.

- An asterisk (*) beside an item indicates an area for which you should use the envelope system.

Allocated Spending Plan (Form 7)

PAY PERIOD: ____ / ____ ____ / ____ ____ / ____ ____ / ____

ITEM:

INCOME _____ _____ _____ _____

CHARITABLE ____ / ____ ____ / ____ ____ / ____ ____ / ____

SAVING

Emergency Fund ____ / ____ ____ / ____ ____ / ____ ____ / ____

Retirement Fund ____ / ____ ____ / ____ ____ / ____ ____ / ____

College Fund ____ / ____ ____ / ____ ____ / ____ ____ / ____

HOUSING

First Mortgage ____ / ____ ____ / ____ ____ / ____ ____ / ____

Second Mortgage ____ / ____ ____ / ____ ____ / ____ ____ / ____

Real Estate Taxes ____ / ____ ____ / ____ ____ / ____ ____ / ____

Homeowner's Insurance ____ / ____ ____ / ____ ____ / ____ ____ / ____

Repairs or Maintenance Fees ____ / ____ ____ / ____ ____ / ____ ____ / ____

Replace Furniture ____ / ____ ____ / ____ ____ / ____ ____ / ____

Other _____ ____ / ____ ____ / ____ ____ / ____ ____ / ____

UTILITIES

Electricity ____ / ____ ____ / ____ ____ / ____ ____ / ____

Water ____ / ____ ____ / ____ ____ / ____ ____ / ____

Gas ____ / ____ ____ / ____ ____ / ____ ____ / ____

Phone ____ / ____ ____ / ____ ____ / ____ ____ / ____

Trash ____ / ____ ____ / ____ ____ / ____ ____ / ____

Cable ____ / ____ ____ / ____ ____ / ____ ____ / ____

*FOOD

*Groceries ____ / ____ ____ / ____ ____ / ____ ____ / ____

*Restaurants ____ / ____ ____ / ____ ____ / ____ ____ / ____

Allocated Spending Plan (Form 7 – continued)

TRANSPORTATION

    Car Payment   ____/____   ____/____   ____/____   ____/____

    Car Payment   ____/____   ____/____   ____/____   ____/____

  *Gas and Oil   ____/____   ____/____   ____/____   ____/____

  *Repairs and Tires   ____/____   ____/____   ____/____   ____/____

    Car Insurance   ____/____   ____/____   ____/____   ____/____

    License and Taxes   ____/____   ____/____   ____/____   ____/____

    Car Replacement   ____/____   ____/____   ____/____   ____/____

*CLOTHING

  *Children   ____/____   ____/____   ____/____   ____/____

  *Adults   ____/____   ____/____   ____/____   ____/____

  *Cleaning/Laundry   ____/____   ____/____   ____/____   ____/____

MEDICAL/HEALTH

    Disability Insurance ____/____   ____/____   ____/____   ____/____

    Health Insurance   ____/____   ____/____   ____/____   ____/____

    Doctor   ____/____   ____/____   ____/____   ____/____

    Dentist   ____/____   ____/____   ____/____   ____/____

    Optometrist   ____/____   ____/____   ____/____   ____/____

    Medications   ____/____   ____/____   ____/____   ____/____

PERSONAL

    Life Insurance   ____/____   ____/____   ____/____   ____/____

    Child Care   ____/____   ____/____   ____/____   ____/____

  *Baby Sitter   ____/____   ____/____   ____/____   ____/____

  *Toiletries   ____/____   ____/____   ____/____   ____/____

  *Cosmetics   ____/____   ____/____   ____/____   ____/____

  *Hair Care   ____/____   ____/____   ____/____   ____/____

    Education/Adult   ____/____   ____/____   ____/____   ____/____

    School Tuition   ____/____   ____/____   ____/____   ____/____

    School Supplies   ____/____   ____/____   ____/____   ____/____

    Child Support   ____/____   ____/____   ____/____   ____/____

Extra copies of this form can be found online at mrc.daveramsey.com/mil-tools.

Dave Ramsey's
Financial Peace
MILITARY EDITION

Allocated Spending Plan (Form 7 – continued)

Alimony   ____ / ____   ____ / ____   ____ / ____   ____ / ____

    Subscriptions   ____ / ____   ____ / ____   ____ / ____   ____ / ____

    Organization Dues   ____ / ____   ____ / ____   ____ / ____   ____ / ____

    Gifts (including Christmas)   ____ / ____   ____ / ____   ____ / ____   ____ / ____

    Miscellaneous   ____ / ____   ____ / ____   ____ / ____   ____ / ____

*Pocket Money   ____ / ____   ____ / ____   ____ / ____   ____ / ____

RECREATION

    *Entertainment   ____ / ____   ____ / ____   ____ / ____   ____ / ____

    Vacation   ____ / ____   ____ / ____   ____ / ____   ____ / ____

DEBTS (Hopefully -0-)

    Visa 1   ____ / ____   ____ / ____   ____ / ____   ____ / ____

    Visa 2   ____ / ____   ____ / ____   ____ / ____   ____ / ____

    MasterCard 1   ____ / ____   ____ / ____   ____ / ____   ____ / ____

    MasterCard 2   ____ / ____   ____ / ____   ____ / ____   ____ / ____

    American Express   ____ / ____   ____ / ____   ____ / ____   ____ / ____

    Discover Card   ____ / ____   ____ / ____   ____ / ____   ____ / ____

    Gas Card 1   ____ / ____   ____ / ____   ____ / ____   ____ / ____

    Gas Card 2   ____ / ____   ____ / ____   ____ / ____   ____ / ____

    Dept. Store Card 1   ____ / ____   ____ / ____   ____ / ____   ____ / ____

    Dept. Store Card 2   ____ / ____   ____ / ____   ____ / ____   ____ / ____

    Finance Co. 1   ____ / ____   ____ / ____   ____ / ____   ____ / ____

    Finance Co. 2   ____ / ____   ____ / ____   ____ / ____   ____ / ____

    Credit Line   ____ / ____   ____ / ____   ____ / ____   ____ / ____

    Student Loan 1   ____ / ____   ____ / ____   ____ / ____   ____ / ____

    Student Loan 2   ____ / ____   ____ / ____   ____ / ____   ____ / ____

    Other _____   ____ / ____   ____ / ____   ____ / ____   ____ / ____

    Other _____   ____ / ____   ____ / ____   ____ / ____   ____ / ____

Allocated Spending Plan (Form 7 – continued)

Extra copies of this form can be found online at **mrc.daveramsey.com/mil-tools**.

Irregular Income Planning (Instructions)

Many people have an irregular income, which simply means that their compensation fluctuates from month to month. This is especially common for the self-employed, as well as commission-based salespeople. While this makes it more difficult to predict your income, you are still responsible for doing a monthly budget!

The Monthly Cash Flow Plan (Form 5) should remain a crucial part of your plan, as it lays out exactly how much money you need to bring home each month to survive and prosper. However, instead of doing the Allocated Spending Plan (Form 7), you will use this Irregular Income Planning sheet.

On this form, simply look at the individual items from your Monthly Cash Flow Plan sheet and prioritize them by importance. Ask yourself, "If I only have enough money to pay one thing, what would that be?" Put that at the top of your list. Then, ask yourself, "If I only have enough money to pay one more thing, what would that be?" That's number two. Keep this up all the way down the list.

With your list in place, you're ready to get paid. If you get a $1,500 paycheck, you will spend that $1,500 right down the list until it is gone, recording the cumulative amount spent in the Cumulative Amount column. At that point, you're finished spending, no matter what remains unpaid on the list. That's why the most important things are at the top of the list, right?

Be prepared to stand your ground. Things usually have a way of seeming *important* when they are only *urgent*. For example, a once-in-a-lifetime opportunity to see your favorite band perform live may seem *important*, but in reality, it is only *urgent*, meaning that it is time-sensitive. Urgency alone should not move an item to the top of this list!

Irregular Income Planning (Form 8)

Item	Amount	Cumulative Amount

Breakdown of Savings (Form 9)

After you have fully funded your emergency fund, you can start to save for other items, such as furniture, car replacement, home maintenance, or a vacation. This sheet will remind you that every dollar in your savings account is already committed to something. For example, it's a bad idea to take money away from car repairs to pay for an impulse Hawaiian vacation, even if you pay cash for it. What would you do if the car broke down the week you got back home? However, it can be okay to reassign the dollars to another category, as long as you do it on purpose and it doesn't put you in a pinch in another category. Keep up with your breakdown of savings every month, one quarter at a time.

Item	Balance By Month		
	_____	_____	_____
Emergency Fund (1) $1,000	_____	_____	_____
Emergency Fund (2) 3-6 months	_____	_____	_____
Retirement Fund	_____	_____	_____
College Fund	_____	_____	_____
Real Estate Taxes	_____	_____	_____
Homeowner's Insurance	_____	_____	_____
Repairs or Mn. Fee	_____	_____	_____
Replace Furniture	_____	_____	_____
Car Insurance	_____	_____	_____
Car Replacement	_____	_____	_____
Disability Insurance	_____	_____	_____
Health Insurance	_____	_____	_____
Doctor	_____	_____	_____
Dentist	_____	_____	_____
Optometrist	_____	_____	_____
Life Insurance	_____	_____	_____
School Tuition	_____	_____	_____
School Supplies	_____	_____	_____
Gifts (incl. Christmas)	_____	_____	_____
Vacation	_____	_____	_____
Other _____	_____	_____	_____
Other _____	_____	_____	_____
TOTAL	_____	_____	_____

Debt Snowball (Instructions)

Now it's time to knock out that debt! List your debts in order, from the smallest balance to the largest. Don't be concerned with interest rates, unless two debts have a similar payoff balance. In that case, list the one with the higher interest rate first. As you start eliminating debts, you'll start to build some serious momentum. These quick wins will keep you motivated, so you'll be able to stay on track.

The idea of the snowball is simple: pay minimum payments on all of your debts except for the smallest one. Then, attack that one with gazelle intensity! Every extra dollar you can get your hands on should be thrown at that smallest debt until it is gone. Then, you attack the second one. Every time you pay a debt off, you add its old minimum payment to your next debt payments. So, as the snowball rolls over, it picks up more snow. Get it?

Redo this sheet every time you pay off a debt so that you can see how close you're getting to total debt freedom. Keep the old sheets for encouragement—or to wallpaper the bathroom in your debt-free house someday!

The New Payment is the total of the previous debt's payment PLUS the current debt's minimum. As these payments compound, you'll start making huge payments as you work down the list.

Debt Snowball (Form 10)

Item	Total Payoff	Minimum Payment	New Payment

Pro Rata Debt List (Instructions)

Pro rata means the fair share, or the percent of your total debt each creditor represents. This will determine how much you should send them when you cannot make the minimum payments. Even if you cannot pay your creditors what they request, you should pay everyone as much as you can. Send the check for their pro rata share, along with a copy of your budget and this form, every month. *Do this even if the creditor says they will not accept it.*

Do you need to use the pro rata plan?

First, use your monthly cash flow plan to determine your total disposable income. Simply write down your income on the line at the top of the form. Then, write down the total you spend on necessities (not including consumer debt) each month. Subtract the necessity expense from the income, and you are left with your disposable income. This is the money you have to put toward your debts.

Second, add up your total amount of debt, not including your home, and write that in the blank provided. Below that, write in the total of the minimum monthly payments on all your debts. If the total of your minimum payments is greater than your total disposable income, you need to use the pro rata plan.

For example, Joe and Suzie have a total debt of $2,000, with a combined total minimum payment of $310. However, this family only has $200 in disposable income each month, which means they do not have enough money to make the minimum payments. So, they will use the pro rata plan to give each creditor their fair share of the family's $200.

How to Use This Form

This form has six columns:
1. **Item:** the name and type of the account.
2. **Total Payoff:** the total amount due on the account.
3. **Total Debt:** the combined total of all your debts.
4. **Percent:** the portion of the total debt load that each account represents. You can calculate this by simply dividing the Total Payoff by the Total Debt for each line.
5. **Disposable Income:** the amount of money you have left after paying necessities.
6. **New Payment:** the amount that you will now send to each creditor. You calculate this by multiplying the numbers in each line's Percent and Disposable Income columns.

The pro rata plan helps you to meet your obligations to the best of your ability. Of course, your creditors will not like receiving less than their required minimum payments. However, if you keep sending them checks, they'll most likely keep cashing them. We have had clients use this plan, even when sending only $2, who have survived for years.

Pro Rata Debt List (Form 11)

Income   _____

Necessity Expense   − _____

Disposable Income   = _____

Total Debt: _____

Total Monthly Payments: _____

Item	Total Payoff		Total Debt		Percent		Disposable Income		New Payment
_____	_____	/	_____	=	_____	X	_____	=	_____
_____	_____	/	_____	=	_____	X	_____	=	_____
_____	_____	/	_____	=	_____	X	_____	=	_____
_____	_____	/	_____	=	_____	X	_____	=	_____
_____	_____	/	_____	=	_____	X	_____	=	_____
_____	_____	/	_____	=	_____	X	_____	=	_____
_____	_____	/	_____	=	_____	X	_____	=	_____
_____	_____	/	_____	=	_____	X	_____	=	_____
_____	_____	/	_____	=	_____	X	_____	=	_____
_____	_____	/	_____	=	_____	X	_____	=	_____
_____	_____	/	_____	=	_____	X	_____	=	_____
_____	_____	/	_____	=	_____	X	_____	=	_____
_____	_____	/	_____	=	_____	X	_____	=	_____
_____	_____	/	_____	=	_____	X	_____	=	_____
_____	_____	/	_____	=	_____	X	_____	=	_____
_____	_____	/	_____	=	_____	X	_____	=	_____
_____	_____	/	_____	=	_____	X	_____	=	_____
_____	_____	/	_____	=	_____	X	_____	=	_____

Dave Ramsey's
Financial Peace
MILITARY EDITION

Monthly Retirement Planning (Form 12)

Too many people use the READY-FIRE-AIM approach to retirement planning. That's a bad plan. You need to aim first. Your assignment is to determine how much per month you should be saving at 12% interest in order to retire at 65 with the amount you need.

If you save at 12% and inflation is at 4%, then you are moving ahead of inflation at a net of 8% per year. If you invest your nest egg at retirement at 12% and want to break even with 4% inflation, you will be living on 8% income.

Step 1: Annual income (today) you wish to retire on: _____

Divide by .08

(Nest egg needed)equals: _____

Step 2: To achieve that nest egg you will save at 12%, netting 8% after inflation. So, we will target that nest egg using 8%.

Nest Egg Needed $ _____

Multiply by Factor   X _____

Monthly Savings Needed = _____

Note: Be sure to try one or two examples if you wait 5 or 10 years to start.

8% Factors (select the one that matches your age)		
Your Age	Years to Save	Factor
25	40	.000286
30	35	.000436
35	30	.000671
40	25	.001051
45	20	.001698
50	15	.002890
55	10	.005466
60	5	.013610

Dave Ramsey's
Financial Peace
MILITARY EDITION

Monthly College Planning (Form 13)

In order to have enough for college, you must aim at something. Your assignment is to determine how much per month you should be saving at 12% interest in order to have enough for college.

If you save at 12% and inflation is at 4%, then you are moving ahead of inflation at a net of 8% per year.

Step 1:   In today's dollars, the annual cost of the college of your choice is:

Amount per year $ _____

X 4 years = $ _____

(hint: $15,000 to $25,000 annually)

Step 2:   To achieve that college nest egg, you will save at 12%, netting 8% after inflation. So, we will target that nest egg using 8%.

Nest Egg Needed $ _____

Multiply by Factor   X _____

Monthly Savings Needed   = _____

Note: Be sure to try one or two examples if you wait 5 or 10 years to start.

8% Factors (select the one that matches your child's age)		
Child's Age	Years to Save	Factor
0	18	.002083
2	16	.002583
4	14	.003247
6	12	.004158
8	10	.005466
10	8	.007470
12	6	.010867
14	4	.017746

Dave Ramsey's
Financial Peace
MILITARY EDITION

Credit Card History (Form 14)

CARD NAME	NUMBER	ADDRESS	PHONE #	CLOSED	WRITTEN CONFIRMATION REQUESTED	WRITTEN CONFIRMATION RECEIVED
Visa	1234 561989 12	1234 Poplar Grove, suite 130	123-456-7890	09/21/06	09/21/06	11/21/06

Extra copies of this form can be found online at **mrc.daveramsey.com/mil-tools.**

Dave Ramsey's
Financial Peace
MILITARY EDITION

Credit Card History (Form 14)

CARD NAME	NUMBER	ADDRESS	PHONE #	CLOSED	WRITTEN CONFIRMATION REQUESTED	WRITTEN CONFIRMATION RECEIVED

Dave Ramsey's
Financial Peace
MILITARY EDITION

Insurance Coverage Recap (Form 15)

TYPE	COMPANY	PLAN ID #	POLICY #	AMOUNT	AGENT	PHONE #
Term life	ABC Insurance	1234 567989 12	1234 567989 12	$450,000	John Smith	456-7890

Mortgage Information

TYPE	COMPANY	PLAN ID #	POLICY #	AMOUNT	AGENT	PHONE #

Dave Ramsey's
Financial Peace MILITARY EDITION

Insurance Coverage Recap (Form 15)

PHONE #	AGENT	AMOUNT	POLICY #	PLAN ID #	COMPANY	TYPE

Mortgage Information

PHONE #	AGENT	AMOUNT	POLICY #	PLAN ID #	COMPANY	TYPE